FETTERS OF HATE

D1612880

On their wedding day the formidable Nick Vakotis told Helen, 'Remember always that you're mine. Should another man ever enter your life, then you'll wish with all your heart that you'd never been born.' What would happen if he discovered that Helen's real reason for marrying him was to forget Paul, husband of her best friend?

FETTERS OF HATE

BY

ANNE HAMPSON

MILLS & BOON LIMITED
17-19 FOLEY STREET
LONDON W1A 1DR

First published 1974
This edition 1974

© Anne Hampson 1974

ISBN 0 263 716082

Made and Printed in Great Britain by
C. Nicholls & Company Ltd.
The Philips Park Press, Manchester

CHAPTER ONE

HELEN Crawford had just arrived home from Greece where for the past two years she had held the enviable post of private secretary to Spiros Palisides, one of the top executives of the Vakotis Shipping Company whose head office was in Athens. The heartbreaking decision to throw up her job had been made quite suddenly, after the totally unexpected attentions of the owner of the firm had made it impossible for her to remain in his employ.

It wasn't marriage he wanted, Nickolas Vakotis had frankly told her. When eventually he married it would be to one of his own countrywomen.

"They know their place," he had said with faint mockery, and with typical Greek arrogance in his piercing black eyes. "Western women make themselves far too troublesome."

At first, Helen was not too perturbed by the interest of the dark Greek who, having come into the office when her boss was away on holiday, had asked to see his secretary. The first swift glance, beginning as an indifferent and negligent one, had become a most disconcerting stare as those all-examining eyes had slid from her face to her neck and then to the curves alluringly accentuated by the perfectly-cut dress she wore. The examination included the rest of her body, right down to her ankles, slim and dainty above pretty sandals of pale blue leather, matching the colour of her dress. Having lived so long in Greece Helen was by no means unused to this kind of stare, and although she was invariably embarrassed, and would colour faintly, she soon regained her calm. And so it was with Nick Vakotis. But she was soon to realize that his interest was by no means transient; he came into the office every day for the next fortnight, while her boss was still away, and he asked her out to lunch. She had refused, but his invitation had become an order. He then wanted to take her out to dinner and, because she was anxious to hold on to her job, and also feeling convinced everything would be back to normal once her boss had returned, Helen agreed to dine with Nick.

The climax had come when, instead of taking her back to her flat in Athens, Nick had taken her to his house outside the city – or rather, one of his houses, as he had others besides the palatial home to which he took her on that unforgettable evening after they had dined at one of the most expensive hotels in the capital.

"The name suits you," he had said, an ardent note creeping into his deep and resonant tones. "Helen ... the incomparable!" And before she could even grasp what was happening she was in his arms, being kissed as she had never been kissed before. The sensuous lips were inescapable no matter how she struggled; the iron-hard body was pressed too intimately close.

"Let me go! How dare you –?" The rest was smothered as he claimed her lips again; and he lifted her into his arms and carried her to a low couch and laid her down on the luxurious cushions.

"Stop struggling!" The full lips thinned suddenly and the black eyes scorched into hers. Nick Vakotis, wealthy and handsome ship-owner, was not used to being repulsed by any woman, least of all one of his employees. "You knew what to expect when you came here –"

"I didn't come of my own accord! You brought me here – when I expected you to take me home, as you've always done before." She was white to the lips, staring up into a dark and ruthless face, the face of a savage with the most evil intent.

"You'll not regret being my pillow friend," he told her, bending to take his fill of her lips again.

"Your –? Oh, how *dare* you make such a suggestion! I'm not –" That was as far as she got, for the rest was cut short by his kisses.

"Stop struggling," he repeated, but more persuasively this time. "You were made for love, Helen . . . let me look at you." His eyes travelled over every contour of her lovely face; he saw the blue veins under the peach bloomed skin of her temples, the high cheekbones, the soft mouth, rosy and tempting. The high forehead, usually so serenely unlined, was creased now as if its owner were in acute pain. The big blue eyes, slanting at the corners, slightly but most enchantingly, were dilated with fear. Nick pushed his long sensitive fingers through her pale gold hair, and brought a few strands to his face, giving a small sigh and shaking his dark head as if some wonder had been performed before his eyes. "Two years you've been working for me . . . and I never met you. Two years wasted –"

"Let me go! You dare not molest me – not an English-woman! I'll go to the police!"

"Police?" imperturbably and with a lift of one fine straight eyebrow. "My child, you seem to forget who I am."

Yes, she had forgotten. The mighty Nick Vakotis

could get away with murder!

Helen knew she would be indebted to fate for the rest of her life, for without its intervention all would have been lost, there being no possible hope of escape from the amorous intention of her dark and merciless captor.

But just when she had accepted the inevitable an imperious ring at the doorbell stayed the hand that would have slipped away the shoulder-strap of her evening gown, and Nick straightened up, a heavy frown darkening his forehead.

Without a word he strode from the room, and only then did it strike Helen that he had sent the servants off somewhere and that in consequence there was no one to go to the door.

"Nick, my love!"

"Mother . . . what in the name of Hades are you doing here at this time of the night!"

"You're not pleased to see me? I have come to Athens for a visit and so I stay with my son. It is natural, is it not?" The language changed and Greek was spoken, but Helen understood. "Well, ask me in, if you please! I am famished and thirsty – with the long journey and no food on the train." A sudden pause and then, slowly, with each word emphasised, "You're alone, my son . . .?"

"I have one of our employees here, that is all."

"Male or female?"

A dry laugh, tinged with amusement, and then,

"Female. Let me take your coat."

"Female. An employee? That's a new one! Take me to her –" Another sudden halt. "She is in a state fit to be seen?"

At this Helen, who had swiftly taken advantage of the

interruption and not only got to her feet but also flung on her wrap and grabbed her handbag, walked into the hall where the two were talking.

"I'm quite fit to be seen, madam!" she flashed in English. "And if you'll kindly step to one side I'll leave!"

Startled, the woman obeyed. Unable to resist, Helen threw a glance at Nick; his eyes actually laughed at her, but his voice was a distinct warning as he said, very softly so that the words seemed to come from under his breath,

"This isn't the end, Helen. On the contrary, it's only the beginning," and he followed her to the open door and added finally, "I have never desired any woman as I desire you . . . and I shall not rest until you're mine."

Without a word she ran down the steps and along the pathway towards the tree-lined road where a taxi was procured without any trouble. Thankfully she sank into the upholstery, not daring to allow her mind to dwell on what would have happened had not Nick's mother chosen to ring the doorbell at that particular moment.

The following day he had come to the office and after sending for her he told her, quite frankly, that he wanted her for his pillow friend, and that he would make it worth her while. It was then that he added the words about eventually marrying one of his own country-women.

"However, you'll reign supreme until I tire of you," he told Helen, so blandly and so confidently, just as if he was sure she would comply with his suggestion – even after the events of last evening. "And also I shall set you up in a pretty villa, which will remain your property when the time comes for us to say good-bye."

Helen had looked him over contemptuously, safe in

the knowledge that he could not harm her here in the office.

"I suppose," she could not resist saying icily, "that you're used to women accepting your offers both with eagerness and anticipation." She had not meant to voice a word like anticipation and while she herself flushed a little he was displaying a small hint of amusement.

"I have every reason to believe they enjoy my – er – company, as I enjoy theirs."

Although she had been most emphatic in her refusal of his offer he had nevertheless gone away in a mood of confidence and, swayed by a sort of wild panic that took possession of her, she told her boss, immediately on his arrival back at the office, that domestic circumstances necessitated her returning to England at once, and she was unable to say when she would be back.

"I'm very sorry to lose you, Miss Crawford," he had said regretfully. "However, if ever you should want to come back a post will be found for you. You have some holiday money due to you, so if you leave me your address it will be sent on to you when we have worked out how much it is."

"Thank you."

The panic had remained right up to the moment of taking off from the airport.

"Darling!" her mother had gushingly greeted her six hours later. "It's so nice to have you back again. You will make your home with us, won't you?"

A glance at her stepfather, dandified as ever, with his waved hair and prim little smile, his weak chin and rather watery grey eyes and Helen said guardedly,

"I'll stay for a while, Mother, but –"

"Harold wants you to, dear, just as much as I. We know why you went away in the first place and we're now willing to be more understanding, aren't we, Harold?"

He nodded and produced another thin smile.

"Of course we are."

How, wondered Helen, had her mother come to fall for a fop like Harold Lynch? At the time of the marriage Helen had given it six months. That was almost three years ago and the couple seemed more comfortable than ever. Everyone to his or her own choice, thought Helen, whose mind suddenly, and totally against her will, brought in a picture of Nick Vakotis, tall and slender, with powerful shoulders and an inflexible jaw. Classical features, cold as stone, and as strong; eyes like black pitchblende, and as hard. The hawk-like nose fitted in well with the rest of his features, and with his jet black hair, thick and healthy and waving slightly from a low and noble forehead. The whole combined to form an image so formidable that even here, in the safety of her home, Helen felt a shiver run the whole length of her spine. Nevertheless he was a man, she thought, glancing again at the dandy who was her stepfather.

"You never told us why you suddenly decided to come home?" Mrs. Lynch was bustling about between the kitchen and the living-room, preparing the evening meal. "You'd always seemed to be so happy in your job over there."

"I felt I'd had enough," replied Helen non-committally. "It isn't a good thing to remain in one job too long."

Harold Lynch looked at her.

"I've never changed my job since I was fourteen years of age," he supplied, "and it hasn't done me any harm."

11

Nor any good, Helen could have commented, but of course she desisted.

After the meal was over Helen washed the dishes, her mother and stepfather having decided to go to see the film that was showing at the local cinema. So much for her homecoming, she reflected ruefully. But there never had been much of a relationship between her mother and herself, and there was less now that her mother had married a second time.

"I'll go and see Fran," she decided, and immediately telephoned her.

"Helen, how nice to hear your voice! So you arrived home all safe and sound, then?"

"Yes. You got my letter, obviously?" Helen had written a hurried note two days before leaving Athens and had not been sure it would arrive before she did.

"This morning. What a surprise, and a very pleasant one! Where are you now?"

"At home. I thought of coming round. Paul doesn't come on a Tuesday, you've told me?"

"That's right; he works as a barman at the Golden Goose, just to make a bit extra for the marriage kitty!"

"You must be getting excited?"

"Bubbling over with it — But come on round! We've a lot to tell one another."

An hour later Helen was sitting in the cosy living-room of the Sandimeres' suburban home, chatting with Frances, who had been her friend for over ten years.

"So that was why you left so suddenly?" Fran looked sympathetically at Helen after listening without comment to the explanation she had asked for. "The rotter! But so many men are, these days. They just seem to think that all women are theirs for the asking. A house, he offered you – oh, it's horrid! What does he think you are, a – a –?" She broke off and with the trace of a smile Helen said,

"They call them pillow friends over there, and I afterwards learned that, with a man of Nick Vakotis's standing – he's a millionaire ship-owner – women consider it an honour to be chosen."

"Then he must have received his first set-down by your refusal?"

"I expect so." Helen became thoughtful. "I wonder what he felt like when he knew I'd gone? I couldn't get a flight for two days, so I left my flat – just brought in a man and sold the lot – and moved into an hotel, where he couldn't find me."

Her friend was frowning at this.

"You weren't afraid he'd abduct you, or anything dramatic like that?"

"I wouldn't put it past him. He's a man with a high degree of determination. I gained the impression that when he wants something he'll stop at nothing to obtain it."

"Well, thank goodness you're safe. He can't get what he wants now, so he'd better go and hunt elsewhere."

The subject of Nick Vakotis was then dropped and Frances talked about her fiancé, Paul, whom Helen had not yet met.

"He's so handsome," declared Fran. "I don't know how he ever came to fall for me."

"And I don't know how he could do otherwise, once he'd met you," returned Helen loyally, her gaze taking in

13

the small pretty face and soft grey eyes. "Tell me some more. How did you come to get to know each other in the first place?"

"It was at a party. But at first he didn't take much notice of me and he had only one dance with me all the evening. Then we met again at the tennis club, and again at the regatta. It was then that he asked me to go out with him – and that was it. We've been going steady ever since." Fran's eyes glowed as she became quiet for a moment. "I can't wait to be married, Helen! It's interminable, this waiting!"

Helen laughed. At twenty-three she was still completely heartfree, never having met anyone she could take to sufficiently to go out regularly with, let alone consider marrying.

"You haven't much longer to wait. I'm glad I'm home for the wedding."

"So am I. You'll be a bridesmaid?"

"But isn't that all arranged –?"

"I'm having three bridesmaids, but I'd very much like another," she said, looking invitingly at her friend. "It'll make my day perfect if you're a bridesmaid."

"All right," agreed Helen, "I'd love to oblige."

"You'll adore Paul. He's just perfect!" A small pause and then, "Why can't we have a little get-together this coming Saturday? They do dinner-dances at the George and Dragon now; we could go – my brother will come as well, so there'll be four of us."

"Fine. How is Thomas, by the way?"

"The same as ever. I wish he'd find himself a nice girl."

"Don't look at me," laughed Helen. "Tom and I like

14

each other as friends, but there's no stronger draw than that."

"Oh, well," sighed Fran resignedly, "if I can't have you for a sister I can still have you for my best friend."

Best friend. . . . The two words hammered in Helen's brain when, a fortnight later, she at last admitted that what she felt for Fran's fiancé was something she was experiencing for the first time in her life.

And Paul himself . . .?

"Helen, why haven't we met before?" This had been asked on their first meeting, and even though it was said in a light and jocular vein both Paul and Helen had definitely felt some strange emotion creeping over them. Paul danced with her and she sensed a tautness about him; she herself was so deeply affected by him that it was a relief when the music stopped and she could withdraw from his arms.

Two days later Paul telephoned her.

"We've arranged to go out again," he told her, feigning a casualness which did not in any way deceive her. "Fran enjoyed it so much the other night that she wanted a repetition."

Helen had hesitated, under no illusions as to who it was who really desired a repetition. Fran was too intent on saving money to wish for another outing at the George and Dragon, where prices were about the highest in town. However, Helen had at last agreed to go with the other three and this time Paul danced with her much more than he should have done. Tom had cast one or two odd glances from Paul to Helen, and she had noticed the frown that had creased his brow. Fran was starry-

15

eyed and so happy that she failed to notice anything unusual – since, when Paul danced with Helen, Tom danced with her.

The day after this dinner dance Paul called round at Helen's home during his lunch hour break. He was taking a stroll, he said, and so he decided to drop in for a few minutes.

"I suppose you're looking for a job?" he said, his admiring eyes fixed most disconcertingly on her lovely face.

"I've applied for one," she answered, her pulse racing and every nerve tingling. What was it about Paul that made her feel this way?

"I hope you get it." He and Helen were alone in the house and without warning he moved from the chair she had given him and settled himself beside her on the couch. She edged away, filled with anger against herself as well as Paul.

"I might decide to go abroad again," she said in haste, the idea coming to her suddenly. "I feel I shall become restless if I stay here too long."

His eyes had shadowed; he said, a husky note in his voice,

"Helen, don't go away. I couldn't bear not to see you again –" His words were cut as Helen stood up. Her voice was clipped and abrupt as she said, aware that her face was pale and that the palms of her hands were damp,

"You'd better be going, Paul. You have to be back at work by two, you said?"

"I'm not going back today!"

She had turned away from him, but she twisted round again, staring at him.

"Certainly you're going back," she told him sternly.

"I want to talk to you, Helen," he began desperately, "before it's too late –"

"We have nothing to talk about!" There was a strangled note in her voice that could not possibly escape him. His eyes fixed hers as he said,

"There's plenty for us to talk about, and you know it just as well as I. Helen, I can't go through with this wedding!"

Helen was white now, and trembling, but she was also resolute.

"Paul," she said gravely and with an unconscious touch of pleading, "go away. You and I have known each other only a few days –"

"It's love at first sight," he broke in urgently. "I knew it the moment I was introduced to you – and you knew it too. Deny it if you can!"

She shook her head.

"I – don't believe in love at first sight."

"It's happened, Helen," he insisted, standing up suddenly and coming close to her. "Fight it you must, naturally, because Fran's your best friend. But it'll beat you! It's too strong for either of us –"

"Go away," she cried, crossing the room towards the door. "Go away, I say!" And without even waiting to see if he would do as she asked, Helen fled up to her bedroom and, closing the door, she turned the key in the lock.

Every day until the Saturday he telephoned, each time reasserting his intention of breaking off his engagement.

"I shall never marry you – never!" she told him vehemently. "So breaking off your engagement won't do you a scrap of good!"

And at the end of a fortnight Helen, having to admit

that she was most deeply affected by Paul, but at the same time unwilling to admit that what she felt was love, decided to go down to Birmingham where another friend had a flat. Lily had lately written to Helen, saying that as her flatmate had left her Helen would be welcome to a bedroom should she be unable to settle at home.

"I know how much you detest your stepfather," she had written, "and so if you don't want to stay at home there's room for you here. Jobs are easy in the city."

Fran was naturally a little upset by the news that her friend was to leave so soon.

"But you'll still be my bridesmaid, of course." A statement. Helen could find no plausible excuse for changing her mind about that and she resigned herself to one more meeting with Paul. And after that? It would be the end of her friendship with Fran. There was no other way, decided Helen, who was convinced that with time, Paul would forget all about her and the interlude of a mere fortnight that had caused such havoc to his emotions.

Fran had never looked more attractive. Although not possessed of any kind of classical beauty she was inordinately pretty for all that. She lacked the firm character lines which typified Helen's features and which invariably caused men to turn their heads, but Fran had about her a fragility that was most appealing and, watching her at the wedding reception, glancing so often at her handsome bridegroom, Helen sent up a little prayer that Paul would take good care of her.

Helen and Paul danced together, but only once.

"I'm leaving early," she told him. "I have to catch a train."

18

"You could have stayed the night up here." Grim the tones and accusing. "Fran's mum would willingly have put you up – and you do have a mum of your own, remember."

Helen made no reply. The closeness of him stirred some emotion, but, determined as ever not to admit that it was love she felt for him, she managed to thrust this emotion away, quelling its insistence.

The music stopped. Paul looked down at his partner and said,

"If only it had been you –" And that was all, for Helen broke away and less than ten minutes later she was in a taxi, once more running away from a man.

It was only six weeks later that, having answered a knock on the door, Helen gave a little gasp and exclaimed,

"Fran! What are you doing here?"

"I'm alone," whispered Fran huskily, "so you needn't look around for Paul."

Helen's heart turned right over; how she retained her cool and inquiring veneer she would never know. But she did, asking – even as she stood aside to allow her friend to enter the tiny hall of the flat – the reason for Fran's visit.

"I had to come to you, Helen –" Without warning Fran burst into tears. "I c-couldn't go t-to Mother. She'd be too upset." Turning as she uttered these words, in despairing tones that sent an icy chill down Helen's spine, Fran leant against her friend and wept unrestrainedly. Helen's arms went about her, the chill that passed through her setting every nerve quivering.

"Tell me what's wrong?" she urged, holding Fran

19

away and using her own handkerchief to dry her cheeks.

"Paul . . . oh, Helen, you won't believe it, but he wants us to part!"

"Part?" Helen's mouth went dry. She experienced a deep surge of guilt while at the same time knowing full well that no guilt could possibly be attached to her. She had acted honourably, moving away – putting many miles between Paul and herself. She had been willing to lose Fran's friendship in order to avoid any further meetings with Paul. "I don't understand?" she said questioningly, voicing what would naturally be expected of her. "Sit down, dearest Fran, and tell me all about it."

"Paul was strange right from – from the first night," admitted Fran, managing to stem her tears. "I thought it was just the fact of being married – you know, the re-adjustment? It's difficult to make, for some people. I was dreadfully unhappy, Helen, but I knew he –" She broke off and the tears began to fall again. Without speaking Helen handed her a tissue, watching as she dabbled at her eyes with a hand that trembled uncontrollably. "I *thought* he loved me," Fran continued eventually. "But I was wrong." She stopped and looked at Helen, as if she had discovered all at once that she wasn't evincing a sufficient amount of surprise, or indignation – or both. Startled, Helen immediately adopted an attitude suitable to the occasion, frowning heavily and shaking her head in a gesture of disbelief.

"Go on," she pressed. "I can't imagine his wanting to part, Fran."

"He was strange, as I said. And as the days and weeks passed I had to admit that there was something drastically wrong with our marriage. I had to speak about it at last. He w-went out and – and g-got drunk." Sobs shook Fran's slender body and, slipping an arm about her shoulders, Helen drew her close, comforting her as best she could although she herself was very near to tears. "When he came home – so late that I thought he wasn't ever coming home again –" Fran broke off, lowering her head as it occurred to her that she was talking somewhat wildly in saying she thought Paul had gone for ever. "He said – said that he was in love with someone else – someone he'd met a few months ago, before the wedding." She looked up, her vision obviously blurred because she pressed the tissue into her eyes several times. "I asked him who it was, but he wouldn't say. I can't think who it could be, unless it's someone he works with. He certainly never went out without me while we were courting. He came every night except Tuesdays, when he worked in the pub."

Torn between compassion for Fran and anger against Paul, Helen found great difficulty in framing words. She felt a fraud, a traitor, even.

"You say he wants to part?" she managed at last. And, when her friend dumbly nodded her head, "This other girl – he doesn't know if she'll marry him. He seems to be taking far too much for granted –"

"He says she loves him; he knows it although she hasn't said so. She's free; so Paul says – says that if – if we can have a divorce –" Sobs racked Fran's body again and she was unable to continue. Helen could only hold her close, softly cursing the whole race of men. None of them was any good, she decided, her mind switching to the dark and arrogant Greek who was just as vile as Paul, but in a different kind of way.

21

"I'll make a cup of tea," said Helen practically when presently her friend's sobbing ceased. "You came to me. . . . Do you want me to talk to Paul?" And what a talking to she would give him! thought Helen, gritting her teeth.

"I don't know. I just came to you because you're my best friend. As I said, it wasn't the thing to trouble Mother, not at this stage. She'll have to know, of course, later, if Paul insists on the break-up of our marriage."

"The marriage can't break up – it *can't*!"

"He seems adamant," Fran was saying as Helen left the living-room and went into the kitchen. Lily was spending the week-end with her parents and Helen was alone in the flat. She invited Fran to stay the night but, distraught at the idea of Paul's being free to go out with this unknown girl, Fran said she must return that evening.

On her return with the tea tray Helen found her friend a little more composed. She was not so tensed, but she still sat erect on the couch, her mouth trembling and an occasional spasm jerking her body as a dry sob escaped her, the aftermath of her violent fit of weeping.

"Do you want me to talk to Paul?" Helen inquired again, and after a slight hesitation Fran nodded her head.

"Not that I think it will do any good," she added, her face creasing piteously. "He's so determined, as you'll see for yourself." Helen made no comment, but poured the tea and handed a cup to Fran. "I was telling you," Fran went on after sipping her tea for a few quiet seconds, "that Paul says that if we can have a divorce it will be simple for him to marry this girl, as she herself is free."

"That," put in Helen grimly, "doesn't mean that she'll consent to marry him."

"She will – I think. Paul seems very sure of her."

"Paul appears to have become quite heartless," was Helen's conclusion, spoken in the same grim tones. "His conduct's unforgivable." Helen was almost sure that anything she herself had felt for Paul must now be dead, killed both by her compassion for her friend and her utter disgust at the behaviour of her husband.

"I still love him, and I always will." Miserably Fran passed her cup to be refilled as Helen held the teapot poised. "I can't take it in at all. He was so wonderful to me until – until . . ." Fran's voice faded as she began to concentrate. "I can't think just when the change occurred, but I did notice something very slight even before our marriage. When I really noticed the change, though, was – was on our wedding night." With difficulty she succeeded in holding back the tears. "Just imagine, Helen, he was making love to me and thinking about another girl –"

"Stop!" The one word was wrung from Helen before she could prevent it, the idea of what she had just heard being most repellent to her sensitivity and the fineness of her own character and ideals. Surely nothing was more loathsome than for a man to make love to one girl while his mind was on another. And when that other happened to be Helen herself – She cut her thoughts, shuddering slightly. And because Fran was looking askance at her she resolutely made an attempt to regain her composure. "I can't bear to think about it," she said, hoping that would satisfy her friend. It did, and after a while Helen suggested they go out somewhere to lunch. Fran shook her head forlornly and Helen decided to make some sandwiches and coffee. This they had and, after having rung the railway inquiry people about the times of the trains Helen said she would go back with Fran and speak to Paul that very evening.

"Will you? Oh, Helen, I'm so very grateful to you. You've no idea how I was hating the thought of making the journey alone. It was awful coming – with my mind all the time on the conviction that our marriage had failed and that I was soon to find myself alone."

"You won't find yourself alone." Helen kept the grim confidence out of her voice, since she had no wish to find herself faced with awkward questions. "I'll talk to Paul, and I'm sure he'll change his mind about the divorce."

"You really think so? He – he did l-love me once. . . ."

"I really think so," returned Helen reassuringly, and was gratified to see the haunted look disappear from her friend's soft grey eyes.

CHAPTER TWO

"At least one of us is free, and that reduces the difficulties!" Paul spoke in fierce and emphasised tones, his eyes fixed unwaveringly on Helen's face. He and she were alone, Fran having gone over to spend an hour with her mother while her husband and Helen talked together. It had been past nine o'clock when they arrived at the neat little semi-detached house to which the newlyweds had gone after their marriage; Fran, stiff-voiced, had given her husband a brief explanation, then left the house. Helen had stared at Paul with undisguised contempt; his eyes had held both admiration and a sort of sullen defensiveness. No sign of contrition marked his handsome features, and once again Helen thought how despicable men were. It was enough to turn any sensible woman away from marriage altogether.

"Why you should assume that I would marry you, were you free, is quite beyond my comprehension," she told him icily. "Your confidence is incredible!"

"That attitude won't go anywhere to convincing me that I'm wrong in believing you'll marry me when I'm free. Fran's your best friend and in consequence you're being noble and loyal and self-sacrificing. But your love will win, once I'm free. Why I ever went through with the marriage in the first place I don't know. It was sheer hell, standing there at the altar, vowing to love and cherish a woman I'd already ceased to love –"

"That's not true," she broke in, greatly distressed because Paul himself was quite plainly suffering. "You did love her, and still do! What you felt for me was mere infatuation – or something," she added vaguely, since she herself could not explain what it was that had come to them. All she did know was that this meeting with him left her cold and impassive, devoid of all emotion or longing other than the urgent desire to put things right for these two who, she was almost sure, would have been sublimely happy had she not made her untimely appearance on the scene. This belief strengthened her conviction that it was mere infatuation – or something equally incidental – which Paul had felt for her. "You might as well accept, once and for all, that I shall never marry you –" She paused in order to give strength to her next words, "I shall never marry you, Paul, because I don't love you and I never could love you."

"That's a lie!" he raged. "A damned lie. I'm not a fool; I know how you felt that day when I called at your house. You had to run away because your feelings for me were getting the better of you. But had I not let you run away, had I taken you in my arms then, and kissed you –"

"I'd not have hesitated to slap your face," she broke in, but unfortunately blushing at the same time. It had been a tense moment, she recalled. But she was quite certain in her mind that she would never have allowed Paul to kiss her. Fran's sweet face would have intervened, and so would Helen's own sense of honour.

"That's another lie," he averred, seizing on her blush and assuming it to be a sign of guilt following the utterance of an untruth. "You love me, Helen, please admit it." He was beseeching now, both with his eyes and his voice. Strangely, Helen felt nothing but contempt for him, her pity having already dissolved.

"I do not love you," she affirmed. "So you might as well forget you ever met me. I've decided not to communicate with Fran any more, so you and I need never meet again." Her cool calm voice seemed to take him aback, but only for a few seconds. He reaffirmed his conviction that she was being loyal and self-sacrificing, and predicted she would come round once he had his divorce.

"You're really going to ask Fran for a divorce, knowing full well that I shall never marry you?"

"I know full well that you will. You're free. If you were married it might be different; the problem would be greater, the obstacles more formidable. But as it is, with you being totally unhampered, the way won't be too difficult."

"Paul," she reiterated with slow deliberate enunciation, "I *do not love you!*"

With a negligent wave of his hands Paul dismissed this, causing Helen's temper to rise, and her colour also.

"I know you love me and nothing – nothing, Helen – will convince me otherwise. I shan't tell Fran that it's you I love – not yet, but I *am* determined to have a divorce, and as quickly as possible." A small pause and then, "I intend leaving her within the next week or so."

"You can't. . . ." But Helen's voice faded; she saw without a vestige of doubt that Paul meant what he said. "I shan't marry you –"

"I'm quite confident that you will –" He broke off, turning as his wife entered quietly, her eyes searching those of her friend who, averting her head, could only say,

"I'm terribly sorry, Fran, but I've failed . . ."

Barely a week had passed since that night of frustration and failure when, having just taken a bath, Helen heard the doorbell ring and, slipping a robe over her powdered body, she fastened the belt and went through the hall and opened the door.

"You –!" Helen just stared in blank bewilderment at the man on the landing.

"Your mother kindly provided me with your address," said Nick Vakotis suavely, "and here I am. Well, Helen, aren't you going to ask me in?" The black eyes flickered over her; the keen nostrils took in the delightful perfume of expensive talc – his own Christmas present, since he had always provided a sum of money for gifts for the staff.

"Yes – no!" Chaotic nerves and a thudding heart; legs that had gone suddenly weak, and a dampness collecting on her forehead. Automatically she plunged her hands to the edges of her bathrobe, and clutched them tightly.

"Mr. Vakotis," she stammered, "wh-what are y-you – I m-mean – what have you c-come for?"

The dark Greek looked at her silently for a long moment before a suspended smile broke over the handsome yet formidable features.

"I came to ask you to marry me," he replied calmly, flicking a hand in a short of commanding gesture, indicating that she should step to one side and allow him to enter the flat.

"M-marry y-you?" she echoed in high-pitched tones which even to her own ears were unrecognisable. "You – you must be m-mad!"

"I was never saner, my dear Helen." A small pause. "But let's not discuss so delicate and important a matter on the doorstep." Another flick of his hand bringing no response, he added in some amusement, his eyes once again roving over her, "You'll catch cold, my dear."

His knowledge of her nakedness beneath the robe acting as a spur, she jerked from her stupor and would have slammed the door in his face, but a slender, perfectly-shod foot was there to prevent it and the door swung inwards again. Desperately she looked around, frantically and without purpose, since no help could possibly be forthcoming, the flat downstairs being temporarily unoccupied. If only Lily would appear! But she had an over-

28

time duty this evening and would not be home for another couple of hours.

"Go away," she begged, white to the lips. "Go away, I say! I'll – I'll scream!"

"I'm not here to harm you," came the quiet, reassuring promise. "You seem to have forgotten: I've just asked you to marry me – No, don't interrupt," he added firmly as she opened her mouth. "I'm on an honourable mission. I want you for my wife."

Dazedly she shook her head. This was some fantastic dream – no, not a dream but a nightmare!

"Go away," she cried again. "I don't want to marry you – or – or to have anything to do with you. I can't th-think why you should come, all this way!" Her accents had reached that higher pitch again and she saw him frown a little. "You're mad," she repeated, but immediately added, in nothing louder than a whisper, "or else I am."

"Helen," he said in a very soft tone, "I'm coming in."

"No – I shan't let you!" But she was lifted right off her feet and, not daring to kick or struggle lest the robe should fall open, she lay quite passive in his arms until, having kicked the door closed and passed through the hall into the living-room, he put her back on her feet.

"My dear Helen," he said in some asperity, "why all this melodrama? Is it your habit to make a fuss where no fuss is necessary?"

The calm and mildly-spoken words left her bereft of speech. This situation was not real; it couldn't be! The wealthy and handsome ship-owner whose reputation was well known, who could from all accounts have any woman he desired, just for the asking . . . this man to come all

29

the way from Greece to see her, Helen Crawford, an ex-employee in his firm, and to ask her to marry him. . . . No, it wasn't happening. She must soon wake up and thankfully breathe freely again.

"I should go and get dressed." The soft words came on a thread of amusement; Helen heard them but still felt she was in a dream.

"Please go away," she faltered, fear still plucking at her nerves despite the rather anxious expression on his face and the reassuring words he had spoken to her. "I don't want anything at all to do with you."

He saw that she was terribly afraid and said, almost gently,

"You'll feel more like talking when you've dressed. Go and do so. I'll just sit here, I promise." Again the thread of amusement in his tone, but his regard was grave. "You've absolutely nothing to fear, Helen. You might have gained the impression that I'm a rake, but I'm an honourable man for all that –"

"Honourable!" she ejaculated as memory flooded in. "Was it honourable to act as you did that night? It was your intention to – to. . . ." She let her voice trail away, swift embarrassment sweeping over her and bringing hot colour to her cheeks.

Nick actually laughed.

"No, it wasn't," he denied. "Not to force. I mean –"

"Oh, yes, it was!"

"Pardon me, it was not. It was certainly my intention to persuade, but never to force."

She said, anger prevailing over her embarrassment,

"It would be interesting to know what your methods of so-called persuasion are!"

At this he gave another laugh, and only then did she realize what she had said.

"Would you like me to demonstrate?"

She lowered her head, but – very gently – he raised it again.

"Go and get dressed." And this time it was an order, softly given but firm for all that. Helen left the room and entered her bedroom. There was no lock on the door and on hearing his footstep in the living-room she grabbed her clothes and ran into the bathroom, slipping the bolt with nerveless fingers and making far more noise than she intended. He'd be laughing again, she thought, wishing her heart would cease its wild and painful throbbing.

By the time she was dressed and had combed and brushed her hair, she was much more calm and in consequence her mind more clear; she realized that had the man meant mischief he most certainly would not have allowed her to come in here and get dressed. This thought was so reassuring that she was able to forget her fear and dwell more rationally on his proposal of marriage.

Desire. . . . Nothing more . . . and yet why marriage? There were many other women available who could satisfy his desire.

At length she emerged and re-entered the living-room, where she stood just inside the door and stared at him across the space separating them. Formidable in spite of the half-smile playing about his features. That mouth . . . how many lips had it kissed? she wondered – kissed with passion and ruthlessness and demanding mastery. Marriage? He must be quite out of his mind even to entertain the idea that she would accept his proposal.

31

"Come here." Soft words and yet commanding. He had been seated, but now he rose to his feet, dominating the small room by his height and splendid physique.

Automatically she crossed towards him, as if propelled by some mechanical appliance that not only set her in motion but also thought for her.

"Mr. Vakotis," she began, when he interrupted her.

"The name's Nick," he murmured. "If I'm going to be your husband then you'll have to get used to saying it, I'm afraid, since you can hardly keep on calling me Mr. Vakotis."

She shook her head and said,

"If you will tell me what this is all about?"

He frowned as if in pain.

"My dear Helen, you are not obtuse. I wanted you before; I'd have had you had not Mother appeared –" He stopped and the black eyes flickered with sudden mirth. "You must have sent up a prayer of thankfulness at fate's timely intervention."

"I was certainly most fortunate."

"But I've just said I would never have used force."

"You've also said you – you would have – have had me. . . ." She faltered over her words, as well she might, for this conversation was of the kind in which she had never dreamed she would ever be involved.

"I'd have had you, most certainly – by persuasion."

She looked disdainfully at him, the last remnants of fear having left her.

"How confident you are!"

"Experience of women has given me confidence in my capabilities."

32

"Nicely phrased," she retorted, and Nick laughed, a humorous laugh that caused her eyes to remain on his face. There was no denying it, she mentally conceded, Nick Vakotis was just about as attractive a male as anyone would ever see. This, plus his great wealth, must inevitably attract the women, and it was really no wonder that he had so bloated an opinion of himself.

"You're so very beautiful," he murmured, staring into those slanting, liquid blue eyes. "It's no wonder I desired you; many other men must have done so too."

She instantly thought of Paul and a deep frown crossed her forehead. Nick began speaking again, going back to the sentence he himself had interrupted.

"As I was saying, I wanted you before, but as fate decreed that I should not have you at that time I naturally accepted defeat – or I meant to accept defeat," he amended. "But if you remember, I said I desired you as I've never desired any other woman; I also said I'd never rest until you were mine." He paused a moment and then, tilting her chin only seconds after she had averted her head, "I couldn't get you out of my thoughts, Helen, and although marriage has never occupied my mind very much at all, I suddenly knew that, as I obviously could not get you any other way, I must offer you marriage." No humility – indeed he was as arrogant and confident as ever, but there was in his voice a touch of persuasion, and, she thought – but could not be sure – a note of anxiety.

She could only stare at him for a long while, conscious of the warmth of those long brown fingers, sensitive fingers, she had previously noticed, sensitive yet strong.

Strangely his touch was not abhorrent to her, a circumstance which in no small measure surprised her. At length she found herself saying,

"I can't marry you, Mr. Vakotis," and she went on to add that she was fully aware of the honour she should be feeling, at which the shadow of a smile touched the full, sensuous mouth.

"Tell me," he said, ignoring the last part of her little speech, "what reason have you for declining my offer of marriage?"

"I don't love you," she answered simply, and saw his straight black brows lift in some surprise.

"I didn't expect you to," he said.

"People do marry for love," she reminded him.

"In your country, yes," he readily agreed, then added, "But not in mine."

"But I am English," she pointed out, and he nodded his head, though abstractedly, and she had the impression that it was an automatic gesture, and that his thoughts were elsewhere. He spoke at last , saying she was the first woman he had ever considered taking for his wife, and that if she did consent to marry him she would know and enjoy all the comforts of wealth, and the prestige of being the wife of a man who was well respected.

"Even though you might yourself be in some doubt about this," he added as an afterthought and with a faint smile.

"You have a reputation," she said. "I heard about it after – after – the incident."

The faint smile remained.

"A man's morals don't affect his prestige or his integrity." Helen made no comment and he said forcibly,

34

"You must marry me, Helen. This question of love is quite absurd, at least to me –"

"Because in your country marriages are arranged – for the most part. You don't trouble yourselves about love."

He inclined his head in agreement.

"I've been honest as to the reason why I want you for my wife –"

"Because you obviously couldn't get me any other way," she put in, voicing his own words.

"Correct. I knew I must offer you marriage."

Helen had to cut in again, to say curiously, and with a total absence of embarrassment that amazed her,

"Your desire for me was so great that you decided to go to the lengths of marriage?"

"Haven't I just said so?" She made no answer and he continued, "I've also said that, in your case, troubling yourself about love is absurd. The question of love surely can't be so important as that of money, security and prestige?"

It was no use trying to make him understand, she realized. In his country, where marriages were arranged, love rarely entered into the partnership. It could come afterwards – in fact, Helen knew of two Greek couples who had found love after marriage, and most ideally happy they were because of it, but in the main the marriage was purely one of convenience, providing the husband with an extra possession and the wife with security.

She looked at Nick, going over what he had just said. So calmly and dispassionately he dismissed love, and she knew he was considering her foolish in the extreme for paying heed to anything so unimportant – and unnecessary – as love when all these other advantages were hers, just for the taking. She did stop to wonder how many women, in her place, would have refused Nick's offer of marriage.

"It so happens that I prefer to marry for love," she told him quietly at last.

"You already love someone?" sharply and with a distinct rasp of harshness creeping into his voice. Helen felt a chill in her spine and shuddered. The man's face was a dark mask and there was something unmistakably evil about it, as he stood there, the pale yellow glow from the wall light falling upon it. She suddenly knew why she had shuddered: this man would be a fiend if under the influence of jealousy.

"No, I do not already love someone." She saw the mask lift and the handsome lines were once more revealed.

"Then, my dear, there's no reason why you shouldn't marry me." He shrugged his shoulders. "Love never lasts anyway – you must have noticed this, among your friends and acquaintances?"

"You seem so very sure," she said, but secretly admitting that what he said was true in the main. Couples started off in love, but sadly drifted apart and either separated eventually or existed in near misery simply because neither had the courage to make the break.

"Of course I'm sure." He looked at her and she knew he was cherishing the hope that she would consent to marry him in spite of what she had mentioned about preferring to marry for love.

At last he went away, angry and frustrated at his failure to bring her round to his way of thinking.

"I'll leave you my address," he said, and wrote down

the name of a famous hotel in the city. "Contact me if you change your mind."

"I shan't do that." But she accepted the piece of paper from his hand. His dark eyes met hers, then slid over her entire figure. She turned from that all-examining and unsmiling stare and opened the front door. "Good night," she said, and he merely nodded curtly and left her.

The following evening he telephoned her, saying he was not leaving England without seeing her again.

"Let me take you out to dinner," he asked, and of course she instantly refused. "You have my word that you'll come to no harm," he promised and, impelled suddenly by some force over which she had no control, she agreed to meet him the following Friday.

Meanwhile, Helen had received a letter from Paul, who wrote that he was leaving Fran in ten days' time, having procured a flat which he could occupy as soon as the present tenant left. He would then tell Fran who it was that he wished to marry, when he gained his freedom.

The letter naturally resulted in a flood of despair sweeping over Helen, but there was worse to come. The very next day she received a letter from Fran saying she was expecting a baby and, immediately telephoning Paul at his office, Helen was shocked to hear him say,

"Yes, of course I know about the baby! But it makes no difference. This thing is out of my control. What I feel for you is such a driving force that I can't rest until I've rectified the mistake I've made. I can't live with her when it's you I love!"

"I shall never marry you," she cried wrathfully. "You're taking too much for granted!"

"You're being noble again, but I'm no fool. You'll not

37

hesitate to marry me once I'm free. What we feel for one another is too strong for either of us. We knew, the first time we met – deny it if you can!"

She made no attempt to do so, for her heart had begun to thud painfully as if in anticipation of some impending fearful incident. An idea had flashed across her mind, leaving behind this disturbance which was rapidly enveloping every nerve and vein in her body. There was only one way of ensuring that Paul gave up the idea of marriage to her. . . .

Swallowing convulsively to relieve the choking dryness in her throat, Helen heard herself say,

"You're not leaving Fran yet, though?"

"It'll be soon. I get the flat in a week's time. I wrote the other day and told you about it."

"Yes." She tried again to remove the terrible parched sensation from her throat, but failed. "A week. . . . You won't say anything to Fran in the meantime – about me, I mean, and the divorce?"

"No." A strange silence fell. "You sound ill – or something? Are you all right?"

She rallied and said,

"I'm fine, Paul."

"You yourself have just mentioned the divorce." He sounded exultant, she thought. "Obviously deep within you you know it has to be – for our happiness."

She made no reply to this, but merely bade him good-bye and rang off.

For a long time she stood, staring down at the receiver, but seeing nothing. It was as if a cloud had fallen, enveloping her . . . like a shroud, she thought, a great shuddering sensation passing through her. Marriage without love,

38

and to a dark, formidable Greek whose only interest in her was her body. She would be a possession, a pretty toy bought for her husband's enjoyment.

Six days later she again telephoned Paul. She would have preferred to pass on her news direct to Fran and let her convey the information to Paul, but as they had no telephone at home she was compelled to ring Paul at his work.

"This is a pleasant surprise," he began, when she interrupted him.

"I haven't much time, Paul. My husband's waiting for me. We're going out to dinner —"

"Your *what*!" The interruption came over on a loud but laughing note. "Your husband? What sort of a joke is this? Some absurd scheme to make me change my mind? Helen, you know you want me just as much as I want you, so let me get on with putting things right for us. Why did you ring?" he then asked, obviously quite unperturbed as yet.

"To ask you to convey the news of my marriage to Fran, and to tell her I'll write as soon as I get to Greece. We're leaving on the ten-thirty plane in the morning." Her quiet but clear and precise voice had its effect. A deep silence fell and she began to wonder if Paul were still at the other end of the line. Then his voice came over to her, a sort of fear in its depth, mingling with disbelief and the first signs of anger.

"What the hell are you talking about? Married? Married? Greece? Explain, for God's sake!"

"Nick and I were married just a few hours ago. . . ." Her voice faltered away to a mere whisper and after a painful pause she began again. "At noon we were mar-

39

ried. I met Nick in Greece – in Athens when I was working there. He came over and asked me to marry him. We're leaving England tomorrow, as I've said, and I shan't ever be coming back – unless it's for a holiday, that is." She scarcely knew whether or not her words were coherent; she hoped they were. She also hoped there was no reflection of her misery in their depths.

"Is – is this true? Am I hearing aright?" Fury was rising. She said quietly,

"Absolutely true."

"But you love *me* –!"

"If I loved you I shouldn't have married someone else, should I?"

"You're not in love with that damned Nick – or whatever you said his name was!" A pause and then, "Is he English?"

"He's a Greek."

"A foreigner? You'd never marry a foreigner!"

Impatiently she told him she was certainly married and mentioned her husband's surname. She went on to repeat her request that Paul would tell his wife to expect a letter soon, and she ended by expressing the wish that he would now be able to settle down to married life with Fran and to look forward to the birth of their child.

"So you're married. . . ." A sort of groan came over the line, but it was followed by angry invective and the declaration that she had sacrificed the happiness of all three by her impulsive action in marrying; she would regret it in less than a week and would then herself be desiring her freedom. "I never dreamed you'd allow your friendship for Fran to carry you to these lengths!" he blazed. "You've married him because you love me, no matter what you say! You knew that you'd betray Fran if you didn't find some form of escape –!'"

"Good-bye, Paul," she cut in impatiently. "I must ring off, as my husband is waiting."

"Helen, don't! I want to speak to you –"

Once again Helen stared at the receiver, which she had just replaced. But this time she was not staring with unseeing eyes, as vividly before her was the mental vision on her husband's expression as he had placed the ring on her finger. Austere and arrogant he had looked – and undoubtedly triumphant. He had got what he wanted – another possession, a possession which he firmly believed his money had bought!

CHAPTER THREE

THE lovely island rose from out of a blue mist as the plane descended towards it. Green hills took shape, bright in the spring sunshine. Valleys of olive trees formed darker patterns opening out to the aquamarine sea; white clouds moved swiftly across the sapphire sky, creating shadows to soften the more austere aspects of the landscape.

From her corner by the window Helen glanced sideways at her husband's rigid profile and her nerves fluttered, out of all control as she visualized the ordeal which would soon be upon her.

She and Nick had spent the night at an hotel but had occupied separate rooms, Nick deciding he wanted his marriage consummated in the more romantic atmosphere of his own villa on the beautiful island of Mytilene. The decision, though more than welcome, had nevertheless amazed her, as she would never have credited him with such nicety of feeling or control of desire. He had come smilingly to the breakfast table, bidding her good morning and enquiring if she had slept well. Half-way through the meal he had said,

"Our honesty with one another as to the reasons for marrying should go far to ensuring a smooth path." He had been referring both to his own frank admission that desire alone had prompted his proposal of marriage, and to Helen's equally frank admission that she had after all been tempted by his money and position. This latter was of course untrue, but as Helen was disinclined to mention Paul the explanation she gave sufficed in the absence of anything better. Accepting it with complete satisfaction, Nick was plainly considering the bargain a fair one, being beneficial to each of them, although in vastly different ways. Helen had made no comment on what he said and after a long pause Nick had then uttered his never-to-be-forgotten words, spoken across the breakfast table in low vibrating tones, while his black eyes held hers fast in their commanding gaze, "Remember always that you're mine, Helen. Should another man ever enter your life then, believe me, you'll wish you'd never been born."

Helen had shivered involuntarily, but Nick's manner, changing swiftly, had resulted in a return of her composure ... until, half an hour later, having been called to the telephone just as she and Nick were about to leave for the airport, she had picked up the receiver and heard Paul saying, after informing her he had got the name of the hotel from her mother,

"This isn't the end, Helen! I'm not the man to accept defeat. You married him because you love me! Did you tell him that you've merely used him, and that your heart is given to another?" He had paused, but Helen found herself quite unable to speak. "I shall follow you! Wait until I have my divorce. . . ." Aware of her husband coming towards her from the desk where he had been having a word with the receptionist, Helen replaced the receiver on its rest. She was deathly pale, with Paul's final words ringing in her ears. Had she made this sacrifice in vain? Time alone would tell, but she tried to believe that all would come right for Fran, and for the baby that, at present, was unwanted by its father.

"We're landing." Nick's voice brought her back to the present and she forced herself to respond to the smile he was offering her. "You've been daydreaming, my Helen. What about?"

She shook her head.

"It was nothing of importance, Nick," she lied, and, glancing down, "The island looks lovely."

"It is rather attractive. I hope you'll get used to living on an island." Half question, and she answered,

"I shall have to get used to it, seeing that it's to be my home."

"Your home for always," he murmured. "You do fully understand?"

She nodded dumbly. What he was impressing on her was that she must now consider herself as his possession,

43

his having bought her with his wealth. And as his possession she would never escape from the island ... never as long as she lived.

The isle of Mytilene – or Lesbos – lying off the coast of Turkey, was one of the largest and most beautiful of all Greek islands, being thickly forested and enjoying an especially attractive silvery light which threw the entire landscape into unusual brilliance so that everything stood out with breathtaking beauty and clarity. Mountains in the north and south of the island enhanced its charm as did, in a very different way, its avenues dripping with wisteria and other flowers, its picturesque villages and its view of the Asiatic coast.

Nick lived in the north of the island, at Mithimna, a spectacularly-situated town abounding with old houses in the Turkish style, and alleyways and arbors interlaced with flowers.

Having driven from the airport in his long low car Nick said at last,

"That is our home, Helen – up there on that hill."

She stared, giving an audible sign of appreciation.

"It looks lovely!"

"I'm sure you'll like living there. I have other places, as you know –" Breaking off to smile with sudden humour, he slanted her a glance, clearly interested in her expression. She kept an impassive face and his lips twitched again. "I expect you'll always have unpleasant memories of the house in Athens? However, we'll not be going there often. I prefer Mytilene because the tempo of life is so slow." He paused a moment, negotiating an acute bend in the road. "The inhabitants of Mytilene are said to be the gentlest of Greeks; they're also reserved in manner and not so excitable as the majority of my people."

"Gentlest," she repeated mechanically. And she added without thinking, "You yourself don't come from Mytilene originally?"

Nick laughed and shook his head.

"No, Helen; I come from Athens. I'm not one of the gentle types you'll find here."

She made no response to this, but concentrated on where they were going. The car climbed all the time, until a flat-topped hill was being negotiated. The villa, low and white and sprawling, nestled among gardens filled with exotic trees and flowers. Away in the near distance could be seen a swimming pool, sheltered on three sides by tall swaying palms and shrubs of lesser height but gayer colours. The whole aspect was one of nature's perfections, with a grove of Judas trees spreading away from the grounds of the villa, and across the still dark sea the clearly-outlined mountains of Turkey, gleaming in the bright golden rays of the afternoon sun.

Three servants were in the hall, smiling by the open door and flashing numerous gold fillings between them.

"Helen, meet Costas, whose duties include some gardening. He grows delicious vegetables –" The man's smile broadened at this; Helen bowed her head slightly and said "How do you do?" The next to be introduced was Julia, the housekeeper, then Katina, a younger woman whose duty it was to keep the house clean. All three were dark-complexioned and stout, with deep-set eyes, almost as black as those of Nick. Foreigners all. . . . Helen felt depressed, and a long way from home. And silently she cursed the day she and Paul had ever met. "Katina will show you your room," Nick was saying, and with footsteps that dragged a little Helen allowed herself to be led away, along a wide thickly-carpeted corridor to a room almost at the end.

She had been in it less than five minutes when her husband knocked and entered, without waiting for permission to do so, and Helen was frowning slightly when she looked across at him. His straight brows lifted a fraction, and the full mouth went a little tight.

"Something wrong?" he asked, coming closer.

"No – of course not." Her nerves began to flutter, in unison with the dull thudding of her heart against her ribs.

"Come here," commanded Nick, stopping a short distance from her. His hands were turned palms uppermost and she placed her own against them. His hands closed over hers and she was pulled towards him. "How beautiful you are!" His mouth came down on hers, gently at first but with increasing pressure as the closeness of her body set the embers of desire alight. "My Helen ... mine, all mine!"

She shuddered, but inwardly, and asked herself how she had come to take this particular way out of her dilemma. She could have taken a post abroad, disappearing in the meantime, so that Paul would never have known where she was. Could it be that this tall dark foreigner with the pagan features had by some compelling force held sway over her will so that its strength was impaired? Undoubtedly there was about him a strong magnetic quality that drew even while, paradoxically, it repelled. She could not bear the thought of his body against hers

46

in the intimacy of love. With a sort of panic she glanced around the beautiful room, as if even now she would seek for some secure haven to which she could retreat. But there was none, and never would be.

He was still holding her and she suffered him for a moment that seemed interminable before, with caution and with an apologetic smile, she gently drew herself away.

"I – I want to unpack – and – and take a shower," she said, but saw his black eyes kindle in a way that would have made her tremble had she not determinedly held on to what measure of calm she possessed.

"There's time enough for unpacking –" His voice was husky and edged with a bass-like tone. "I've waited a long time for you –" His mouth claimed hers again and it was with the greatest difficulty that she took this passively, for her whole instinct was to struggle from his embrace. "Helen," he said in a very soft tone as he brought his mouth from hers, "I expect some reciprocation from you." A warning and an admonition all in one. She coloured under his severe and questioning gaze and with a supreme effort offered her lips, parting them in a smile. "That's better," he murmured a moment or two later. "As long as we both keep to the bargain we made we should get along fine."

To her intense relief he went out then, returning to his own room. She stood by the dressing-table, trembling inwardly, and bitterly regretting her marriage. Tightly she closed her hands – a gesture of control, for she wanted to scream. Nerves, she realized with a sense of shock; never in her life had she suffered from nerves. Never in her life, though, had she found herself in a situation like this, a situation where she was directly under the control of another human being, a situation from which there was no means of escape.

As if to increase the awareness of her position the sound of Nick moving about came to her from the aperture between door and jamb. She had an almost uncontrollable urge to close the door, but dared not. Was she afraid of the dark Greek in there? Quite suddenly she knew she was – and the knowledge brought a surge of fury in its wake. This fear was another new experience for her, and after only a moment she was quelling it, her own strength of character rising above it. Yet at the same time she was accepting her position, and resolving to honour her side of the bargain they had made.

A fortnight passed and after the first few days when adjustment was difficult Helen began to settle into a routine which although lacking any form of excitement also lacked the aversion for her husband which she fully expected she would constantly have to hide. Not that she was in any way happy about her situation, just the reverse. She suffered her husband's attentions rather than enjoyed them and, therefore, there was nothing liberal in what she rendered to him. For his part, Nick kept most generously to his side of the bargain, being open-handed with money and lavish with gifts. Helen had a birthday a week after her arrival and she received a diamond and ruby bracelet and the promise of a trip to Istanbul. Also, there arrived a huge bouquet of flowers, the words on the attached card being, "Greetings to my lovely bride, Nick."

Helen had felt strangely alone that day, and the card

attached to the flowers had somehow made her feel degraded. To receive flowers from a man who could not send love with them seemed all wrong; it made Helen feel cheap – like a paid mistress almost.

Nick gave a dinner party in the high, gracious room which was kept for such occasions. Lighted with candles and subdued illuminations from under the pelmets, and the silver gleaming alongside the cut-glass, the room was fit for the banquet of a queen. Helen was arrayed in the most beautiful and expensive gown, her hair having been taken up on top of her head in the style which Nick had chosen from a magazine, while Nick himself was immaculate in a dinner jacket of superb cut and style.

The guests were all Greeks but spoke excellent English, which was the language used entirely during the evening. Many were the comments on Helen's beauty; and the congratulations extended to Nick were received graciously but without any real sign of enthusiasm. Of a surety Nick was the cool aloof type of man whose inner feelings and emotions were kept trapped under an armour which, decided Helen, no one would ever penetrate – neither man nor woman.

"This marriage was sudden indeed," one man said, looking questioningly at his host, but all Nick said in reply was that it was not sudden at all as Helen had worked in the office at Athens for two years. This manner of carrying off a deception was cool and faintly arrogant, and used though she was becoming to the suave and even tenor of her husband's personality Helen was herself taken by surprise. This showed as she caught her husband's eyes and a little while later he whispered in her ear,

"I pride myself on never being taken unawares, my dear. I had the answer ready, should anyone remark on the suddenness of our marriage."

When the last of the guests had gone Nick told her she had been a great success. He spoke unemotionally, just as if he were talking about some business project he had been putting forward to interested spectators, she thought with a frown.

However, as the days passed she accepted her position with a little more ease of mind. After all, a bargain was a bargain, and any pangs of regret on her part would be misplaced at this stage. More thought should have gone into the initial contemplation of the step she was about to take. She should have foreseen that she would never again know what real happiness and peace of mind were.

Nick had had work to do and for several days after the dinner party Helen found herself alone. This solitude she welcomed, spending her time getting to know the house and gardens and the areas immediately beyond; she then went farther afield, becoming familiar with the picturesque town of Mithimna, where she wandered along alleyways bright with flowers, admired the Turkish-style houses with their corbelled walls, strolled along the waterfront watching the gaily-painted caiques bobbing about on top of the rolling waves, and finally walked along the beach, passing artists from Scandinavia who, intent on their occupation, would scarcely notice her, but one young man, who happened to be English, did glance her way and a smile and a nod were exchanged before the young man said,

"Are you from the same part of the world as I?"

The sound of an English voice caused her eyes to light

up and she stopped.

"I'm from England, yes."

"On holiday?"

"No." A small hesitation and then, "I live here."

"Yes? How come? Are you working on the island?"

She shook her head, examining him briefly before voicing her reply. Fair-haired and clear-complexioned, he reminded her a little of Fran's brother. His eyes were deep green – the colour of the sea which he'd been painting, she thought.

"No, I'm not working here. I'm married to a man whose home is here."

"Married to a Greek?" He gave a grimace and added, "Brave girl!"

Her head lifted.

"I'll be getting on my way," she said coldly.

"Sorry," he put in swiftly as she made to go. "I didn't mean to be familiar. Don't go for a minute; I haven't spoken to one of my own kind for about a month."

Helen hesitated. The young man seemed genuinely apologetic, and also anxious to have a chat with her.

"Don't you get many tourists on this island?"

"Later we do, but it's early yet." He looked up into her face and smiled. "You haven't been here long, that's plain."

"No, only a fortnight – well, not quite that long, in fact," she amended on thinking about it.

"You're just married, then?"

"That's right." Her gaze went past him to the sea beyond; the view he had been painting included the mountains of Turkey, she noticed, deciding she rather liked his style. "Can I have a closer look?"

51

"Of course." He stood up as she came closer to the canvas. "I sell my work," he ventured after a moment.

Helen said nothing. Although she liked what she saw she was not yet acquainted with Nick's likes and dislikes and, therefore, she had no intention of committing herself to buying a painting.

"You live permanently on the island?" she inquired at length, and he nodded his head.

"For as long as I can manage to maintain myself by the sale of my paintings. If I can hold out until the tourists come I shall be okay for another few months at least."

"You're satisfied with a life like this – not having security, I mean?"

A rather bitter smile touched his lips.

"Where does one find security in the world today?" he queried cynically.

"I think I know how you feel," she returned, and saw his glance of surprise.

"Here at least one finds peace – and true values. Wait till you've been here a while, and got to know the people. You'll wonder why you didn't find such a place long ago." He talked on, with Helen putting in a few words now and then. She learned that he had worked in a Birmingham office and that fact seemed to sow a seed of friendship, since Helen was able to comment on some of the places he mentioned. However, on leaving him she made no promise to come again even though he urged her to do so.

"I don't usually come so far," was all she said before bidding him good-bye and strolling back the way she had come.

She did go back, nevertheless; her wanderings took her there a couple of days later and they chatted again.

"How about a cup of coffee?" he suggested, when it seemed that she might be deciding to leave him. "I can recommend Starvros's *cafenion* over there." He pointed vaguely – away towards the centre of the town.

"All right," she agreed after a small hesitation. "But what about your things?" She gestured to his easel and paints, and the large canvas bag lying on the sand.

"It'll be all right to leave them here," he replied carelessly, picking up his coat. "Nobody ever touches anything."

They strolled to the *cafenion*, talking as they went. Starvros gave his male customer a smile of recognition and said curiously,

"John, you have beautiful girl-friend today. Where did you find her?"

"She came to me on the seashore," returned John jokingly.

"Like Aphrodite – out of the waves, yes?"

"Not quite, Stavros." Turning to Helen, John said, "Meet Stavros, Helen. He serves the finest fish dishes on the island."

"You come from England on holiday?" asked Stavros, plainly more interested in discovering all about Helen than serving the coffee John had asked for.

"No, I'm not a visitor," replied Helen, trying to adopt a cool manner but faintly troubled lest she should appear a little too reserved. These people were friendly and hospitable; she wanted nothing more than to create a good impression among them, if only for her husband's sake, as he was a most respected citizen of Mithimna.

"Helen is married to Nikolas Vakotis," obliged John, and the Greek's brows shot up in astonishment.

53

"Mr. Nikolas married! But he is the bachelor always! No one think that Mr. Nikolas will ever marry!"

"Well, they're all wrong," returned John, laughing. "This young lady is Mrs. Nikolas Vakotis – and has been for the past few weeks."

The Greek was scratching his head.

"It is not possible – and yet it must be! Why did I not know this thing before now?" He was frowning heavily and John's laugh rang out again.

"You're slipping, Stavros," he teased. "You were always first with the news, but this time it is I who have had to tell you what is happening."

"Mr. Nikolas. . . ." Stavros was now looking most curiously at Helen, just as if he doubted very much that she was married. "He not bother about marriage – everybody know this thing –"

"Stavros!" John spoke swiftly, and admonishingly . . . and a glance passed between the two men. Helen felt the colour rise in her cheeks. Was Nick's reputation known here, as well as in Athens, then?

"I am sorry, Mrs. Nikolas," came the swift apology from Stavros. "I say these things –" He tapped his head. "I say them out loud and I am sorry. I get your coffee. You have with milk, I think?"

"Yes, please."

"I say, I'm dreadfully sorry," began John, looking at Helen across the table. "I hope you're not too embarrassed?"

Helen made no reply whatsoever, but deliberately changed the subject, remarking on the pretty gardens, and the quaint little wooded verandah with its vines and numerous potted plants and its ancient carvings.

John listened, clearly upset by this change in her, for she spoke almost coldly; her face was set, her eyes brittle.

Stavros's appearance with the tray eased the situation, but only slightly. Helen wasted no time on the drinking of her coffee and as soon as John had finished his she rose from her chair and said she must be going home.

She walked away, but knew words were exchanged between the two men as John paid for the drinks, words about her and Nick. . . .

"Must you rush off?" John spoke as he caught her up. "I feel I've fallen in your estimation, and that you're not going to come to see me again?"

"It wasn't your fault." She glanced at her wrist watch. "I really must be off, John. Good-bye –"

"But, Helen –"

"Good-bye," she repeated, and left him.

She was angry inside – angry with Nick for allowing his reputation to spread this far, angry with John for taking her to the café, and angry with Stavros because she knew full well that her marriage would be the topic of conversation in the café for weeks to come.

Nick was on the patio when she arrived back at the villa; he took one look at her flushed face and lifted an eyebrow interrogatingly.

"Has something upset you?" The question, so casually phrased, was somehow like fuel to a fire and the heat of anger spread through her whole body.

"I've been in a café," she said.

"You have?" His eyes flickered uncomprehendingly.

"It's kept by a man named Stavros."

"How interesting." Nick leant back luxuriously and lifted a long brown hand to his mouth, concealing a yawn. Helen's eyes took on a glassy light.

"He appeared to think that, where you are concerned, marriage was not possible."

"He did?" Nick teetered his chair backwards; a dangerous gleam entered his eyes. "How came it that you were discussing me with a man named Stavros?" he inquired softly.

"Do you know him?" She moistened her lips, only now struck by the fact that she had put herself in an awkward position. And so she played for time, her mind working to discover a way of extricating herself.

Her husband's voice retained its quiet timbre as he said,

"I asked you a question, Helen."

She swallowed, her anger dissolving. She spoke in an undertone of reluctance.

"I went for a cup of coffee and he asked me if I were on holiday here."

"Yes?" The black eyes fixed hers disconcertingly.

"I naturally said I lived here – and that I was married to you –" She broke off, colouring faintly as she remembered that it was John who had imparted that particular item of information to the curious café proprietor, and not Helen herself.

"And . . .?" A slanted look now and sent through half-closed lids. Helen swallowed again, disliking intensely his manner . . . and fearing it a little.

"Stavros was astonished at the news of your marriage. He said that you didn't bother about marriage – that everyone knew this." She felt more confident all at once, and the words came easily. "I gathered that your reputation was common knowledge to all the people around here."

"My reputation?" His dark face was incomprehensible – like a mask that conceals every expressive line and curve.

"You have a reputation. I heard about it in Athens, but I didn't expect it to be known on this island." Her tone was now a challenge, but she was on the defensive too, struck afresh by something in the atmosphere that sent a tingle of fear into her heart.

"What exactly are you trying to say to me?" inquired her husband gently after a while.

"I'm telling you that I was embarrassed – dreadfully so!" She was running headlong into danger without fully realizing it.

Nick's eyes kindled, dark and glowering.

"Were you alone when you went into this café?"

"Of course." The lie came swiftly, but she kept her eyes lowered.

"And – quite alone – you began a conversation with the proprietor, a complete stranger to you?"

She gave a shrug.

"He asked if I was on holiday. I told you this." At the injection of a careless note into her voice an ugly light entered her husband's eyes.

"And from that beginning there developed the confidences which led him to speak about my reputation?" Nick's deep rich voice took on a guttural sound . . . like the low animal-growl that puts paralytic fear into a prey.

"I – I. . . ." Helen instinctively stepped back as her husband rose with deceptive languor from his chair.

"Perhaps I sh-shouldn't have t-talked to him," she quivered.

"Afraid of me, are you?" An ineffable pause and then, "Come here, Helen," he added as she took another step backwards.

She automatically glanced at her arms; the fine gold hairs had lifted and she passed her hands over them. Fear such as this was unnatural, she told herself – but Nick was so large, standing there; so overpowering in this attitude of magisterial dominance.

"Nick –"

"Come here," he repeated, his voice quietly compelling.

Helen regarded him defiantly, but coughed to clear her throat. That this was a nervous action she would never for one moment have admitted. Yet her heart throbbed uncomfortably and her pulse had certainly quickened too. In addition, her voice was jerky when she spoke.

"I don't understand what this is all about – this attitude of yours? If it's meant to intimidate me –" She got no further; her arm was taken – and twisted – so that she was brought forcibly towards him.

"*Were* you alone?" The black eyes were narrowed and alert. "Were you, Helen?"

A dart of memory bringing back her conviction that he would be a fiend if under the influence of jealousy, she adopted an attitude of cautious restraint and the lie was repeated.

"I've told you – yes."

A silence fell – an unfathomable, nerve-racking silence during which those pagan eyes seemed to be piercing her very soul.

'If ever I learn that you've told me an untruth –'"

"I haven't," she broke in, desperate now to bring to an end this scene which she in her foolishness had created. "Your suspicions are stupid! Who do I know on this island?" Surely that was convincing enough for him. But those half-masked eyes remained alert, doubtful even. "Don't you believe me?" she faltered, and a long profound moment of total silence followed.

"I've had a great deal of experience where women are concerned," he informed her softly at last. "They look a man in the face and lie." The lips curled in a sneer of utter contempt. "I've yet to meet a female to whom honour is important."

"Perhaps," she said, managing to summon up a modicum of courage, "the ones you favour are naturally those without honour. . . ." Her voice faltered to an uneasy silence. This man possessed too many characteristics of his pagan forebears; it behoved her to take care how she treated him.

His mouth had compressed; she feared for one moment of uncertainty that he would bring up a hand and strike her across the cheek. But she soon realized that he was in full control of himself, that the fury which undoubtedly raged was not to find outlet in any form of physical violence. He repeated his question even yet again, asking if she went alone to the café. In desperation she lied . . . and looked him in the face as she did so. Whether or not he believed her she was unable to ascertain from the inscrutable expression that looked out from his narrowed eyes, eyes that somehow sent a shiver running along her spine so that every nerve in her body was affected.

"Very well," came the unsatisfactory comment, but he went on to express amazement at her lack of reserve and sense of propriety in indulging in conversation with a total stranger, a man who kept a café and who, therefore, would spend half his time gossiping to his customers.

"How dared you discuss me with him?" Nick added finally. "How dared you!" And his grip increased so that his fingernails bit mercilessly into her arms.

"You're hurting me!" The protest was accompanied by the appearance of tears in her eyes. "Leave go of me!"

His hold slackened; she felt sure he hadn't realized just how much he was hurting her.

"I asked how dared you discuss me with this man!"

"I didn't discuss you with him," she faltered. "It all came out naturally, as we – we talked."

"Came out naturally?" He shook his head as if in disbelief. "Your conversation – with a total stranger – reached a stage where you were talking *naturally*?" Helen had no answer for this, simply because it had been John who had begun the conversation, while she herself had scarcely taken any part in it at all. "If this confiding in strange men is common in your country, then it is not common in mine –"

"I did not confide!"

"– and I would advise you to heed my warning," he continued, ignoring the interruption, "and remember this –" Nick looked darkly at her. "I keep my affairs private as far as is possible. I also value my prestige here, where I live. Should it be lowered owing to any action of yours then you're going to be sorry for yourself. Have I made myself abslutely clear?"

"Absolutely," she answered, choking with rage but

maintaining her armour of restraint. Never again would she be so foolish as to find herself in a position like this, was her strong resolve when at last she was able to escape from her husband's anger. She had learned a useful lesson, and she meant to profit by it. The lesson had revealed certain frightening traits possessed by the dark Greek who was her husband, and although it went against the grain to admit that he could put fear into her, she did admit it and, therefore, decided it would be to her benefit to refrain from any act which could provoke him to the state of anger which she had witnessed today.

CHAPTER FOUR

THE trip to Istanbul was proving to be a great success despite the coolness which had developed as a result of the scene of disunity that had been enacted between Helen and her husband. She had felt at first that he would go back on his word and that the trip would not take place. But he had kept his promise, and as the trip was part of her birthday present she made up her mind to appear gracious about it. Nick was indifferent to her enthusiasm, which was enough to cause her to retaliate, but she managed to resist the temptation and in the end had the satisfaction of seeing his indifference dissolve, after which he showed interest in all they saw, and by the time a couple of days had passed the relationship was – to Helen at least – becoming most enjoyable, with Nick attentive and displaying a charm she would never have supposed he possessed; and he would patiently answer all her eager questions, smiling in amusement on occasions and glancing at her with a very odd expression while he teased her about her childish behaviour.

"Oh," she exclaimed in dismay, "am I being childish?"

"I meant it the nicest way, Helen," he was swift to assure her. "Your eagerness and naïveté are quite refreshing."

She glanced up at him from under her lashes, noting the look in his eyes that undoubtedly betrayed a measure of admiration.

"I'm so enjoying it," she told him with a smile. "This bridge fascinates me every time we cross it. How does the traffic ever sort itself out? It's chaotic!"

He nodded, and for a moment they stood still by the side of the rail, watching the miscellany of vehicles crossing the bridge – the famous Galata Bridge where pedestrians mingled with the cars and buses, where donkey-carts dawdled and the drivers of modern fast cars fumed, where women trailed a few paces behind their men, and brown-faced natives carried weighty merchandise upon their backs. An ox-drawn cart pulled up beside Helen and Nick, and a toothless smile flashed from dry brown lips.

"The poverty," murmured Helen with sadness in her voice. "How it does trouble me!"

Her husband glanced down at her with an unfathomable expression.

"These people are used to it," he remarked at length. "They find no hardship in it as, for example, you or I would."

"This poor man's clothes are rags." She spoke in low

tones even though she surmised he would not understand her language anyway. "And look at his hands. They're so toughened by hard work. Why do people have to slave so hard to keep themselves alive?"

"You're in the East," he reminded her. "Things are very different here."

"How fortunate I was to be born in the West," she said fervently, and a low laugh escaped her husband. He was in a most attractive mood, she thought, fascinated by him all at once.

"But you married a man from the East," he said, his rich low voice edged with amusement. "You are of the East now."

A rosy flush enhanced the peach bloom of her skin; Nick's expression became unfathomable again as he stared down into her face. He seemed thoughtful ... and a little puzzled as well. She had the impression that he could not quite understand her, but that he would very much have liked to do so.

"I don't think of myself as of the East," she said at length, noting his look of inquiry as she maintained a thoughtful silence.

"You're of the East now, nevertheless," he repeated, and she caught a note of significance in his tone. What was he saying to her? Was he telling her, in a subtle way, that she must consider herself as his possession — no more important than those meek and humble women who were even now trudging a few paces behind their husbands? He saw her gaze follow them and another laugh escaped him.

"I shall never demand that you walk behind me," he assured her. "I am not quite so autocratic as that."

Helen's blue eyes glinted.

"Nor I so subservient," was her immediate retort.

"I wouldn't have it so," he responded, half surprising her, as she had expected an arrogant and cutting rejoinder. Taking her arm, he moved on and they completed the crossing of the bridge in silence. They were going to Topkapi, the old imperial palace of the Sultans of the great Ottoman Empire, an enormous building housing the priceless treasures collected by a succession of Sultans over a period of several centuries.

Ornate buildings enhanced the extensive grounds — mosques and fountains and high impressive gateways, one of which was used solely by the Sultan.

"The jewels!" Helen just stared, open-mouthed, once they were inside the palace proper. "The Sultans couldn't possibly have known what they were worth!"

"Nor did they care." The suspicion of a smile hovered about Nick's mouth. "Their interests were mainly wars and women."

Helen nodded and murmured unthinkingly,

"The harem. . . ." And then, gazing around her, "How vast it all is! I can't see the necessity for a place of this size!"

"The harem you've just mentioned, for one thing," said Nick in some amusement. "Five hundred wives do take up rather a lot of room —"

"Five hundred?" She blinked at him, too astounded by this information to be embarrassed by his expression. "Five hundred! No, impossible!"

"They were supermen," he laughed, and Helen did then colour, glancing away to where a dazzling array of jewelled swords and daggers and other weapons lay on purple velvet in a glass-topped display case.

"Have I embarrassed you, my dear?" There was no one about and, putting his arm over her shoulder, he cupped her chin in his hand and forced her to look at him. "Yes," he said musingly, "you're quite refreshing. I haven't come across a woman like you before."

Her colour deepened. His body was close and she wondered why she felt no urge to twist away. And how was it that his hand, with its possessive and masterful hold on her face, failed to produce a desire to cast it off?

"I think you're teasing me." She spoke shyly, aware of some new emotion which she could not explain.

"Am I? In what way, my Helen?" He removed his hand; his fingers were drawn fleetingly and caressingly across her flushed cheek. The touch was like the tender breath of a breeze at twilight; Helen felt it long after Nick's hand had been removed.

"No one could have five hundred wives."

"All right. Three hundred then."

"Nor even three hundred."

"Yes, three hundred. The Sultan inherited the wives of his predecessor, you see."

Helen looked suspiciously at him.

"Really?"

"It was the custom."

"They'd be much older than he."

"Some of them might have been," conceded Nick, but added, "If these weren't wanted by the new Sultan he got rid of them by having them tied up in sacks and thrown into the Bosphorus –"

"No!" she interrupted, horror in her voice. "You are teasing me now."

He shook his head. Clearly he was amused by her concern for these unknown women who had died a long time ago.

"It's true, I'm afraid. The Sultans were a barbaric breed." He looked curiously at her. "Surely you've read about the atrocities they committed?"

"One does think of the Turks as rather frightening people," she admitted, "but I never really believed they were any worse than any other race in those days when life was considered of so little value."

A small moment of quietness followed and then, with a light laugh,

"What is this all about anyway? We're becoming far too serious. Let us find something more pleasant to talk of."

They wandered into another vast room, where an array of turbans flaunted emeralds almost too large to be believed.

"The vanity of them!" Helen's voice was edged with disdain. "Men wearing jewels! It seems indecent."

"Jewels should be solely for the female?"

"Don't you agree?"

"In the main, yes.'

"Men can wear a stone in a ring, but as for things like this —" The very lift of her hand was indicative of the contempt she felt. "They must have been feminine to wear jewels in their clothes."

"Feminine?" with a humorous slant of his eyebrows. "Feminine . . . and possessing three hundred wives?"

She had to laugh, and her husband responded. Helen felt inordinately happy without quite knowing the reason.

"Don't you think," said Nick about three hours later,

"that we have had sufficient for one day?"

She nodded her agreement.

"It just drugs you, doesn't it?"

"It is rather overpowering. Come, let us find a nice quiet tea-room where we can relax and get back to realities."

The tea-room was found, in a quiet alley where they sat under a tree and were served by a smiling dusky Turk who spoke excellent English. He wanted to know where they had come from, and asked how long they were staying in the city. Had they seen the Palace, and the famous mosque of St. Sophia and the Blue Mosque? Nick answered politely but with reserve; Helen became acutely conscious of his glances in her direction and she knew that he was remembering that she herself had not practised a similar reserve when talking to a café-owner. But then he was unaware of the real situation; he had no knowledge that she was in fact with an Englishman, John, who did most of the talking.

From the tea-room they went to the Grand Bazaar, which was a fantastic conglomeration of shops running in long alleyways each of which had its own particular name, like "The Street of a Thousand Rope-makers" or "The Street of a Thousand Jewellers".

Masses of tourists surged along these streets, searching for the unusual but finding difficulty in picking out the genuine from the fake, especially where the metal goods were concerned. Helen picked up a copper kettle, black underneath and faintly green in places. One or two dents providing further evidence that it was not a sham, she asked Nick if she could buy it. To her surprise he shook his head.

"It's a fake," he told her, his eyes flickering to the owner of the shop.

"No fake!" the man exclaimed, looking belligerently at him. "All these things old – very old!"

The suggestion of an amused smile lifted the corners of Nick's mouth. He swept a hand over the enormous array of goods – kettles and lamps, gongs and trays and candlesticks.

"All these are genuine?"

"Every one!"

Nick glanced along the street. Outside every single shop were similar masses of copper-ware.

"And all those are genuine too?"

"I not know; I think they are all genuine!"

"Where do they all come from?"

The man glared at him.

"From the houses – the *yalis* of the rich people!"

Nick laughed and, taking his wife's arm, drew her away.

"You embarrassed him," she said.

"He deserved it. These fellows are making fortunes out of the stupid tourists who still believe one can buy old things in these Eastern countries. The real stuff has gone long ago." He glanced down into her face. "Your own common sense should have told you that great masses of stuff like that couldn't possibly be genuine."

"No, I suppose you're right. All the same, some of it could be genuine."

"That's possible," he acceded, "but as the fakes are so excellently done it's risky to buy with the idea that you're getting something really old, and valuable." They had reached a junction and Nick turned into the street of the jewellers. Windows on both sides of the alleyway shone with almost blinding brilliance; here was more so-phistication than was to be found in the streets where Helen and Nick had been strolling up till now. In those streets dark-faced men sat chatting and smoking *narg-hiles* while they watched their stalls, but here in the alley-way given over to the jewellers the owners were inside their shops.

Nick stopped to look in a window; Helen could only stare spellbound, and thinking that here too must exist some fakes, since it seemed quite impossible that so much jewellery could be genuine. But Nick obviously knew that it was genuine because he was showing interest, whereas before he was merely casting an indifferent glance at the merchandise on sale.

"What shall I buy my lovely wife?" Turning his dark head as he spoke, he smiled at her, and allowed his eyes to flicker over her beautiful face, and the delicate curve of her neck. Her short cotton dress was cut daringly low, exposing her shoulders and neck and the hint of other alluring curves – curves on which her husband's eyes had now come to rest. She coloured; this offer of a present had a strangely depressing effect on her, but for what reason she was unable to say. But it brought back the memory of the way she had felt on receiving Nick's flowers on her birthday. She had felt cheap ... like a paid mistress. Later, she had seen herself only as a dolled-up toy which her husband was proudly showing to his friends ... his latest acquisition ... his newly-purchased property.

"I don't want anything." She spoke suddenly, swiftly, and in taut and clipped-off tones which brought a faint look of frowning enquiry to her husband's face.

"Is something the matter?" he asked.

She bit her lip, stemming the impulse to say something cutting, something that would undoubtedly start a quarrel.

"No ... not really...." She turned her eyes towards the fascinating array in the shop window, but she saw none of it; she had no desire to see it. Sparkling diamonds and other precious stones; glittering gold fashioned into every conceivable kind of feminine ornament imaginable. What real value was there here?

"Something *is* wrong, my dear." He seemed anxious, she thought, and looked up into his dark face. His gaze was searching; it took in her tight lips and furrowed brow. "What is it, Helen?"

"Nothing." She shook her head. "Shall we go on?"

"I want to buy you something." But he walked on and for a while no words passed between them. However, he stopped again and, pointing to a sapphire necklace with earrings to match, he asked her if she liked them.

She frowned and shook her head.

"No, I don't."

"No? How about the bracelet, then? A gold bracelet always looks attractive."

"I don't want anything, Nick," she said again. "I'm not over-fond of jewellery."

"You're refusing – actually refusing my offer of a present?" He seemed strangely impressed by her manner, and she realized that always he had been used to buying favours from the women with whom he had conducted his affairs. Her reluctance to accept gifts had come as a complete surprise to him. "You're a strange girl, Helen."

"Perhaps I am." She managed a smile, unwilling to create an even mildly unpleasant situation between her husband and herself. She was enjoying the holiday, was happy in Nick's company, and to spoil this would be folly.

"I would very much like to buy you something," he said, but added with a resigned shrug of his shoulders, "However, if you prefer that I didn't, then I shall respect your wishes."

Her smile deepened; Nick stared for a long moment and then, slipping an arm about her waist, he took her from the brilliantly-lighted window, and all the other jewellers' shops were passed without so much as a glance either from him or Helen.

That night they went to an hotel where there was dancing after dinner. Nick danced superbly, and as Helen was also an excellent dancer they both thoroughly enjoyed the evening, returning to their hotel in the early hours of the morning.

"Why are you so perfect?" The question was voiced in a low vibrating tone within seconds of their entering their bedroom. Nick was standing just inside the closed door, while Helen herself was by the wardrobe, her wrap in her hand. She had been about to hang up the wrap, but had turned on hearing her name softly spoken. The question had followed and pretty colour mounted her cheeks. She knew not what manner to adopt and in her indecision she said flippantly,

"I expect prodigal nature was in a particularly reckless mood when I was being made."

Nick's eyes flickered for one amused second before he strode across the wide room towards her.

"I wasn't joking. I have never met so perfect a creature

as I chose for my wife." Taking the wrap from her, he laid it across the back of a chair. His eyes never left her face – eyes intensely dark, and passionate; the air in the room seemed to vibrate with the immense force of his personality. "My Helen –!" His arms possessed her slender body, crushing it to him; his warm hard mouth arrogantly claimed hers. And in the room was silence, a silence broken eventually by a sigh. "Out of all the women on this earth I found you – most perfect of them all!"

Of them all. . . . A figure of speech, she knew, but unbidden there rose a procession of beautiful women, one after another . . . lovers of her husband. And she was just another – with a different name, of course, but no better than the rest. His wife. . . . A purchased wife, purchased only because she could not be borrowed, for on his own admission he had not initially desired to marry her. He would one day marry one of his own countrywomen, he had told her. They knew their place. . . .

"Nick," she said, endeavouring to withdraw from his ardent embrace, "I'm very tired tonight."

"You want to be alone?" There were two single beds in the room and automatically his eyes flickered to the one on which lay her dainty nightgown, arranged prettily by the maid who had turned down the covers.

"I'm tired," she said again, and this time her voice was sharp. She was not in the mood to give her body just for the passing pleasure of this man whose sole interest in her was desire. Yet she could not honestly admit that she regarded him with even the smallest degree of loathing. He was too magnificent a person for that, too considerate and experienced in his lovemaking, ever aware of important things like respect and gentleness and finesse. No, it was not aversion which caused her inhibitions tonight; it was her own thoughts and the self-disgust which these thoughts had inspired. Nick, however, was not to know this, and at the sharp note in her voice his dark eyes had kindled.

"To use your colloquial English, you're giving me the brush-off." Quiet tones but brittle; Helen swiftly denied this, speaking with a show of indignation that totally misfired, as she should have guessed it would. Her husband's perception was something she should be used to by now. "I'm not inclined to accept your brush-off," he added softly, taking little notice of her protest. "I'm your husband, Helen, and never you forget it." And she was taken to him again, and passionately kissed, just as if he were demonstrating his power over her, in addition to adding emphasis to the words he had just uttered.

She was pale when at long last he held her from him. He inquired if she were regretting her bargain, watching her expression with a steely gaze as she paused before answering him.

"No, Nick, I'm not regretting my bargain."

"You married me for my money, and the security and position that money could give. I married you because I wanted you – more than I have ever wanted a woman in my life. Our bargain was a fair one on both sides. I shall keep my part to the end, Helen, and I expect you to keep yours." The pagan eyes seemed suddenly to be like molten lava, and as destructive. "If ever you should try to break the bond that holds us, then beware. You're mine, and you remain mine!"

"Your – possession." Something rose in her throat –

neither anger nor indignation, but something inexplicably painful.

"If that is the way you wish to put it – then yes, you are my possession."

She turned, twisting from his hold, and walked slowly to the window. The curtains were closed, but she parted them, the scraping of rings on a brass rail making a discordant sound that grated on her nerves. She looked out, over the city with its mosques and minarets, its buildings that were a mingling of the old and the new. The smooth waters of the Sea of Marmara were enfolded in a gauze curtain of misted silver; the same shimmering phantom of moonlight caressed the Golden Horn, that curving inlet of the Bosphorus that formed the harbour. It was a scene of magic – a realm where romance could be born, and flourish. Helen felt her husband's hands upon her bare shoulders; they moved caressingly to her arms and down to her waist, almost encircling it. Warmth penetrated; she closed her eyes, acutely aware of sudden conflict taking place within her. What was happening? This conflict was a subconscious thing, elusive, ineffable. She strained to grasp its meaning and, shocked, she was forced to admit that while her mind rebelled her body desired ... desired her husband, his caress, his mastery, his victory over her. Guilty colour flooded her cheeks and she was glad she had her back to him. What sensual world of carnal love had she entered? Was she no better than the man she had married? How could she desire him without loving him?

"Helen...." The word was a caress; his hands were on her throat and she trembled at the contact. Her whole body strained to turn and feel his arms embrace it; nerves quivered with expectancy — as if heaven itself were near. "My wife...." His lips were on her hair, and as on a previous occasion he took strands of gold and put them to his cheek. "You expect me to resist you?" With a low laugh he turned her, gentle domination in his every act. "You were born for love, and *I* found you. I'm the most fortunate man in the whole world."

"Nick, I —"

"Give me your lips," he commanded, and stood above her, arrogantly above her, waiting for her surrender to his will. A struggle took place within her, but the outcome was predetermined. What unhealthy power did this man exert upon her? — this foreigner from a pagan land, a land where marble gods were worshipped and mystic rites followed by his ancestors. "Helen...." The softly-accented word was an order and a reproof; she lifted her face, powerless to defy him, and went on tip-toe, placing her small hands on his shoulders. Her lips were offered in almost sacrificial humility, and they were possessed, triumphantly. "You — angel!" His mouth moved to her cheek, her temple, her forehead. And then she felt it on her neck; he looked at her and his eyes smiled. "I can go no lower," he said, and tugged playfully at the collar of her evening gown. Her face was flushed; he watched the colour fluctuate — and the light of the victor shone from his eyes. He released her and drew the curtains to-gether, shutting out the lovely Eastern night of moon and stars and a purple velvet sky.

"Nick," she said again, and was interrupted as before.

"What reason you have for making an endeavour to resist me I do not know, nor wish to know. You can't re-sist me, Helen, you know it as well as I."

"Don't say that," she exclaimed. "I would be a poor sort of woman if I could not!"

He only smiled at this, and returned mildly,

"And I should be a poor sort of man if I couldn't break down your resistance." He laughed suddenly, and flicked her cheek with his finger. "Resist, then, my Helen, and let us see what happens."

She lowered her head, but it was not anger or embarrassment that held her in its sway. She was hearing his words, "my Helen", and wondering why she should be wishing they had been "my love".

Nick was taking her hand, drawing her into the centre of the room. With his other hand he slid down the zip fastener of her dress. Motionless she stood there, making no protest when the dress, having been slipped from her shoulders, dropped to the floor. His dark eyes devoured every curve and line of her golden body, clad now in nothing more protective than she would have worn on the beach. Nick shook his head, like someone attempting to shake off the influence of a potent drug.

"My — my nightgown," she managed at last, having fought to escape the net of apathy which his power had woven about her. "P–please pass it t-to me."

Amusement mingled with the ardency in his gaze. God, how attractive he was! How could she ever have hoped to resist charm such as this?

"Shy? Helen, you're the most delightful creature." And he lifted her up and a moment later she felt the smooth white sheet beneath her . . . and her husband's cool clean breath against her face. . . .

CHAPTER FIVE

SHE lay staring at his profile, taking in the finely-chiselled lines and contours. The Athenians carved statues like this; she had seen a great number in the museums during the period she had worked in the city. He stirred and she thought he gave a sigh in his sleep. Her hand came from under the covers, her desire to touch him irrepressible. She gently pushed her fingers through his hair, meaning to put it into order but only tousling it a little more. So thick it was, and slightly waved. He moved presently and turned his head; she withdrew her hand and hid it under the covers again, but it was caught and brought to his lips.

"What have you done to me?" he wanted to know, easing himself up on one elbow so that he could gaze down into her lovely face. "Superlative creature that you are — you have captivated me utterly. I am your willing slave!"

Helen had to laugh.

"You — a slave?" Enchantingly her brows lifted and his gaze, transferred to them, took on a most odd expression. "Do you normally indulge in untruths first thing in the morning?"

"It's the truth."

She shook her head.

"We haven't been married very long, but already I've learned enough about you to know that you'd never be a slave to anyone — and certainly not to a woman."

"You've learned that much, have you? And what else

have you learned about me?"

"You have a temper."

A smile and then,

"What other traits have you discovered?"

"You're possessive."

An emphatic nod to this.

"Anything more?"

"You're generous."

"You won't let me be as generous as I'd like to be." Helen made no comment and he added, glancing meaningfully at her, "You must remember, Helen, that there's a tremendous amount of pleasure to be derived from giving. When you refuse to accept then you deprive a person of pleasure."

She looked up into his face, a frown appearing on her brow.

"I've never looked at it that way," she admitted.

"One must learn to take as well as to give. In my opinion this refusal of one party to accept is the cause of many a broken marriage."

So serious his tone and grave his expression; Helen felt she was learning something very important about her husband at this moment, discovering qualities which seemed to clash with his morals as she knew them.

"Did you really want to buy me a present?" she inquired at length.

"You know very well I did."

"Have you any idea why I refused?" Her hand was taken again and Nick seemed interested in the lovely almond shape of her fingernails. He handled them as one would handle those of a baby newly-born, and with the same expression of wonderment in his eyes.

"No, Helen, I haven't."

She hesitated a moment and then,

"I would have felt cheap."

"Cheap?"

"I can't explain properly," she apologized. "You see, I'm not like all those other women you've had."

"All?" with a raising of his brows and a hint of humour touching the corners of his mouth.

"If you're honest you won't deny that you've had many women. A man doesn't get a reputation for nothing."

After a long moment of thoughtful silence he nodded his head.

"I expect you're right. But what do you mean when you say you're not like the others?"

"They – er – sold their – their favours."

"Exactly?" He looked questioningly at her. "Aren't you selling yours?"

She went a trifle pale.

"Is that what you think of me?"

His eyes opened wide.

"My dear Helen, are you trying to tell me you married me for some other reason than that which I mentioned last night?"

"For money and security?"

"Of course. That was all part of the bargain we made."

"Yes, it was, but. . . ." She allowed her voice to trail away to an uncertain silence, for she had no idea what she wanted to convey to him. She knew only that some change was taking place within her mind, but what it was she was unable to comprehend.

"But what?" He was interested in her hand again, his thumb passing over the delicately-modelled fingers and up to the wrist.

"Nothing, Nick. As I said, I can't explain properly."

"You're a silly girl," he told her presently. "You made a bargain; keep to it and your life will be strewn with rose petals all the way. And now, my Helen, I think we ought to get up, don't you?"

She slipped from the bed and into a dressing-gown, then drew wide the curtains.

"Nick, it's beautiful!" All else forgotten, she turned and beckoned, indicating that he should join her, which he did, slipping an arm about her waist and looking out to where a magnificent colour sheen was being produced by the sun penetrating the early morning mist which lay over the Golden Horn and the Sea of Marmara. Everything appeared to be enveloped in a quivering pearl and coral mantle of gauze. The minarets of St. Sophia and the Sultan Ahmet Mosque shone against the rose-streaked sky, like jewels in a mighty crown. And as Nick and Helen watched, and the sun's rays became stronger, the colours multiplied and the town took on the aspect of a polychromic canvas, but only fleetingly, for as the mist dissolved the colours moved, like the transformation that takes place when the scenery is changed on the stage where a pantomime is being performed. Nick opened the window and through it drifted heady air laden with a sweet aroma from the gardens below. "It's magic! Nick, I do adore mornings like this – and such fantastic scenes! They're worth all the money in the world!" Unconsciously she twisted her head; her face came to rest in the crook of his arm. Glancing up, she caught an odd expression in his eye, and wondered greatly at it. But as he noticed her interest he drew a mask over his face and she was left in doubt as to what that expression had portrayed, since it had not remained long enough for her to keep it in her mind.

He bent to take her lips; she responded, thrilling to his embrace, the nearness of his hard body, the smile in his eyes when at length he held her away and looked deeply into hers. If only she could forget that she had been bought, married for desire alone – and because Nick could not get her any other way – she felt she could be reasonably happy.

"Come, child," she heard Nick say a moment or two later, "it's time we made a move!"

They were going up to Eyüp, and after breakfast the taxi arrived at the hotel. They drove through the city, past the mosques and the quaint wooden houses which intermingled with the more modern buildings, past the narrowest part of the Golden Horn and on to the "city of the dead" where was situated the tomb of Abu Eyüp, friend of the prophet Mahomet himself, the founder of Islam.

All the graves were in rows, stretching away as far as the eye could see. Helen gasped at the immensity of the region of the dead, but Nick explained that everyone wanted to be buried near to the man who had been a disciple of Mahomet.

"Thousands of pilgrims come here," Nick told her. "Moslems from every part of the world. Abu's tomb is a shrine, and Moslems are naturally drawn to it."

After taking lunch in the café they left the city and returned to Istanbul. Dinner and a night club completed another happy day and Helen impulsively thanked her husband when at last they were in their room.

"Don't thank me, Helen," he smiled, taking her hands in his. "I too have enjoyed myself . . . more than I would ever have imagined." The low tones vibrated strangely; she found herself searching his face without knowing what it was she sought. But his expression told her nothing in any case, for a mask was drawn over it and apart from the smile on his lips it remained impassive.

They had been back on the island of Mytilene about a week when Helen, out walking along the waterfront at Mithimna, came across John, who was painting the caiques in the harbour.

"Hi!" he called, and she stopped, though reluctantly. After her denials to her husband that she had had company when in the café, Helen had decided it were prudent to keep away from John. But she could scarcely proceed on her way without having a word or two with him, and when he produced a collapsible canvas stool she felt it would be churlish to refuse to sit down. "I'd hoped to see you before this. What do you do with yourself?"

She frowned at this, for she gained the impression that John concluded that Helen was neglected by her husband.

"We've been away, taking a short holiday in Istanbul," she answered.

"You have?" If he felt surprise he hid it successfully. "How did you like the city?"

"It was marvellous. I loved every minute of our stay."

"I've been there once or twice. I made quite a lot of money from the paintings I did there."

"I should think it's an artists' paradise."

John nodded in agreement.

"The quaint *yalis* fascinated me. I enjoyed the detail which I had to put in." John continued to talk, but Helen was uneasy. Some strange thread of warning urged her to get up and make an excuse for leaving. But as good manners forbade an abrupt interruption she allowed her companion to talk on, telling her of his travels and experiences in the countries he had visited. Then suddenly she saw Nick's car speed past and her heart lurched with dismay. For she felt certain that, out of the corner of his eye, her husband had caught a glimpse of her, sitting there, on the harbour, with the young artist. The lurch settled to a throb of fear as the car slowed down and came to a stop.

"I must go," she said quickly, knocking over the stool as she rose to her feet. "That's my husband." She made a supreme effort to exercise calm, but her nerves were on edge. "Good-bye, John," and without another word she hurried off, towards the man who was already striding out in her direction.

"Who, might I ask," said her husband pleasantly as they met, "is that?"

"An Englishman – an artist."

The black eyes flickered to where John was seated.

"I can see he's an artist. How long have you known him?"

"I – we – er – met a short while ago. . . ." Her voice quavered off to silence as she noted Nick's changing expression.

"A short while ago?" His hard unfathomable stare was fixed upon her and she felt the colour recede from

83

her cheeks. But anger rose alongside her fear. She had every right to speak to one of her own countrymen if she so desired. "How long ago?"

"I met him on the beach –"

"On the beach?"

Helen drew a breath, trying to keep her patience.

"I was taking a walk along the beach one day. John was painting – as he is now – and we spoke to one another."

"John. . . ." Nick spoke thoughtfully, his expression obscure. "You haven't answered my question," added Nick at length. "How long have you known him?" He waited, watching her delicate colour fluctuating.

"About three weeks – perhaps a little less."

Her husband's face became a mask of suspicion.

"Three weeks, eh? That young man," he added pointedly, "frequents Stavros's *cafenion*."

More colour receded from her face, but at the same time the measure of her anger rose and she said with a hint of defiance,

"Have you any special reason for mentioning this fact?"

Sparks entered his eyes suddenly. He said in tones of brusque command,

"We'll talk when we get home," and he strode towards the car, Helen skipping to keep pace with him.

The journey was silent, ominously silent, and despite her determination to preserve a front of courage Helen quaked inside as fear of her husband plucked at her nerve-ends.

Once in the house he turned to her, his mouth tight, his eyes hard and unyielding.

"You lied when you told me you entered that café alone." A statement; much as she would have wished to prevaricate, attempting to deceive him, Helen accepted that this was a waste of time. She swallowed hard before she spoke.

"I had to lie because of your attitude."

"My attitude?"

"Don't pretend you weren't in an angry mood," she almost snapped.

"Which was natural when you'd admitted discussing me with a total stranger!" He advanced towards her and she stepped back. "I said a woman could look a man in the eye and lie to him! So you're no different from the rest?" The black eyes raked her with wrathful contempt. "You were taken into that café by this John – and the three of you discussed me, your husband! You talked of my reputation, as you termed it! What else did you talk about?"

"Nothing – as a matter of fact, I didn't talk much at all."

"No? You mean you sat back and listened to two men discussing me –?"

"It wasn't like that at all. Oh, why did I mention having been in the café?" she cried. "Had I not done so this situation would never have arisen."

"You mentioned it with the intention of bringing it home to me that I did in fact have a reputation," he reminded her, speaking through his teeth. Deep colour had crept up the sides of his mouth and his nostrils flared, more hawk-like than ever. "I warned you that if my prestige should suffer by any action of yours then you'd be sorry for yourself. Do you remember?" So quiet the tone

85

all at once, yet the underlying sinister accents sent shivers running all along Helen's spine. "I asked if you remembered?" he repeated when she failed to answer him.

"Yes – I remember." Her face was white; never had she believed she would find herself so bereft of courage as she was at this moment. But Nick was so tall and overpowering, so frightening in his smouldering fury, so imperious that approach for the purpose of offering an excuse was impossible. "Nick, I –" The gritting of his teeth cut her short. Demanding to know how far the friendship with the artist had gone, he came closer as she spoke, denying that there was any friendship at all. Her wrists were gripped even as she would have stepped back. She cried out at the pain of the pressure he put on to the bones. "You're hurting me, Nick!"

"Hurting you!" he snarled, his face so close to hers that his hot breath fanned her cheek. "Hurting you –!" Deliberately he jerked her wrists, making her start with pain and bringing tears to her eyes. Her heart was thudding wildly, her nerves fluttering about all over the place. "I warned you at the very beginning never to forget that you are mine, and . . . and, Helen," he added in a guttural voice, "do you recall what I said then?" The black pagan eyes bored; the features, evil now and taut, seemed to be enlarged with their nearness to her face. That he meant to have an answer was plain and without hesitation she said, her voice husky and edged with apprehension,

"Yes, I d-do recall what y-you said then."

"Well?"

"You said that should another man enter my life, then I'd – I'd. . . ." She tailed off, anger rising alongside her fear.

"Go on, Helen," he encouraged gently, "finish what you were saying."

Saliva filled her mouth; this and the little ball of anger in her throat prevented speech for a long moment, but she spoke soon enough when, quite deliberately, her husband once again increased the pressure on her wrists.

"You said I'd w-wish I'd never been born."

"Exactly." He moved, but retained his grip on her wrists.

"Another man hasn't entered my life," she told him, the tears trickling from her eyes to her lashes, and hanging suspended there. "I only stopped and chatted to John. He spoke to me as I passed, and as we're both English it was natural that we should chat."

The black eyes narrowed to mere slits.

"You expect me to believe that nothing at all has developed from this first chance meeting?"

"Nick," she said glancing down at his hands, "you're hurting me."

"I asked you a question!"

Her mouth quivered.

"Certainly nothing has developed —"

"Then why were you together in the café?"

"He asked me to have a cup of coffee with him."

"And you went?" Nick looked as if he could not believe what he heard. "You went, knowing what sort of gossip would ensue?" Without affording her any opportunity of replying he went on, the dark eyes wider now, but glowering, "No one on this entire island gossips more than Stavros."

"How was I to know that?" she demanded with a sudden spurt of courage. "In any case, what can he say?"

"Plenty! It'll now be common knowledge all over this island that my wife has been seen in a café with an Englishman! And today – your shamelessly sitting there, in view of anyone passing by! – sitting on a stool like some common fishwife –"

"Oh – how dare you talk like that!" Helen gave a violent wrench and freed herself; but the pain was excruciating and the tears sprang to her eyes again. "How dare you, I say! You shall apologize to me, or I'll never speak to you again!"

His brows shot up at this.

"*I* apologize?" with arrogant astonishment. "I? No, my girl," he went on shaking his head, "it's you who'll apologize. I was just about to order you to do so."

"Order?" The one word came in choked accents as her suspended fury broke through her fear. "You have a lot to learn about me, it seems!"

"And you about me," he promptly returned, his voice quieter than hers. "You have also to learn that here, in my country, a wife is always subordinate to her husband."

"You said you didn't wish me to be subservient," she reminded him.

"The words are not synonymous," curtly and with a faintly contemptuous stare, at what he obviously considered to be her ignorance of her own language. "Subordinate means inferior in importance; subservient means servile."

Her eyes flashed, brittle and hard as glass.

"Isn't that what you want me to be – servile?"

"Helen," he murmured in a very soft tone, "I am not intending to bandy words with you. I'll have your apology, and your promise that you'll not again act in a way that will be likely to cause me humiliation, and then we shall let the matter drop." He paused to regard her warningly. "You've been let off lightly this time, but a repetition of your conduct could have dire results for you." He continued to hold her gaze, his whole manner so lofty and dictatorial that it was impossible for her to crush her anger and recapture her control.

"Don't you dare talk to me like that," she snapped. "I'm not a child!"

His eyes glinted.

"Are you going to apologize?" he inquired gently.

"Most certainly not! I've done nothing for which I consider an apology necessary – whereas you have! And so it's you who'll do the apologizing – and until you do I shan't speak to you!" She had stepped back as she spoke, but of course there was no escape, should he decide to take hold of her again. However, he remained where he was, his height dominating the room, his face taut, his mouth set in a thin straight line.

"Is that your last word?" he asked her, using the same gentle tones.

She merely nodded her head, disinclined to speak when she had told him she had no intention of doing so. His face relaxed, much to her surprise, and a hint of amusement actually touched the corners of his mouth. Nevertheless, his accents held an implacable note when presently he said,

"So there we leave it, do we? Well, Helen, we shall see who capitulates first." And with that he strode to the door and a moment later she was alone, her feelings very mixed indeed, for she knew not whether she had scored a victory or taken a defeat. Perhaps time would tell, she thought, but the more she dwelt on her threat to maintain a silence until her husband apologized, the more she felt that she had done no more than inflict a punishment on herself, since it was most unlikely that Nick would sink his pride and tell her he was sorry. She had fully expected him to make a much stronger stand for an apology from her, but she was now brought to the conviction that her own attitude had placed a trump card in his hand.

"I don't think I was very clever after all," she owned at length, a heavy frown creasing her forehead. "In fact, I've played right into his hands!" The knowledge infuriated her, and this anger increased as she recalled Nick's sudden flash of amusement. Yes, he had grasped the situation at once, seeing much further than she had done — seeing her in a position where she was unable to speak without suffering the humiliation of admitting that Nick had effected a victory by the simple method of withdrawal, the position being rather like that of starving the enemy out, as it were. Well, she decided, the light of determination in her eye, if he thought she would speak then he had a disappointment coming to him! She would remain dumb for ever if need be.

But when making this decision Helen little knew just how difficult would be the carrying out of her resolve. Nor had she realized just how much discomfiture she herself was to undergo, for it was not in the least pleasant sitting opposite to her husband at the dinner table and never a word passing between them. Half way through the meal he went for his book, and from then on she saw nothing but his head — except of course when he leant back so that another course could be served to him by Julia. And after dinner Nick went out to the patio for his coffee, while Helen had hers in the sitting-room on the other side of the house.

The hours dragged; she was already feeling unhappy and lonely, recalling how content she had been when on that visit to Istanbul with her husband. Something had happened to her during that visit, although she had no idea what it was. All she knew was that at one point she had desired her husband – perhaps not with all the force and passion that he desired her, but her desire had been present just the same. She had known a sudden access of pleasure and expectancy when he touched her; she had willingly offered her lips to him, experiencing no wish to draw away when, in triumph, they were possessed.

And now she wasn't even on speaking terms with him.

She heard him go to his room, and now her position loomed more difficult than ever. But surely he would keep to his own bedroom ... or would he? For desire he had gone to the lengths of marrying her; it was unlikely that he would now be willing to put aside the terms of their bargain. In any case, it would hardly be fair. Helen freely admitted this. Theirs had been a business arrangement – both marrying to suit their own ends. The arrangement was permanent; Nick had emphasised this at the very beginning. Once again Helen cursed the day she met Paul – and she cursed herself for not finding some other way out of the predicament. Marriage was so serious a step, and looking back now she was filled with astonishment that she had so readily allowed herself to be steered into it by the forceful Nick Vakotis. At the time she had seemed to have had no will of her own, being dominated by his. It was almost as if he had inherited the power of the ancient gods – the power to do with mere mortals just what they pleased.

At last she rose from the chair she had occupied since dinner, and went outside, to stand for a while on the patio, savouring the still purple night and the feel of the breeze on her face. Already she loved the island, with its vast olive groves and vineyards, its lovely beaches and views, its warm friendly people. The moon, full and incredibly large, hung over the sea, coating it with silver. Stars, brilliant as the finest diamonds, contributed a million points of light to the drowsy landscape; the mountains were proudly draped in robes of silver splendour. All was silent except for the wings of the cicadas; Helen felt peace stealing over her and she sat down in a comfortable armchair. A flying beetle came close to her face, and a huge moth, but she knew no aversion, for the drowsiness of her surroundings was transmitting itself to her and her eyelids began to flutter down. A star slid across the purple heavens and was lost in infinity; a white veil drifted over the moon, lacy and transparent – a filmy cloud brought in from the sea by the breeze. Exotic perfumes filled the night air, heady and potent, like a drug.

With an effort Helen opened her eyes, determined not to fall asleep here but at the same time reluctant to go to her room just yet. She wanted to give Nick plenty of time to go to sleep, as she could not bear to think of his coming to her tonight, not with this disunion existing between them.

But she suddenly became tensed as the sound of his footsteps broke the silence. He appeared before her clad in a dark blue dressing-gown, a shadowed figure that seemed to be an integral part of the night. Her nerves fluttered, reflecting her quickened heartbeats; she felt already the full force of his power even though he was standing some distance from her, in the dimness of the trailing bougainvillaea vine that clung to the pillars supporting the patio roof. He did not stir, and as the tedious moments passed it seemed that despite the fact of his coming out here, he had no desire to communicate with her. Her anger fought to break through the restraint she was having to exercise; nothing would have afforded her more satisfaction than to inquire haughtily what he wanted.

After a while he decided to sit down, and took possession of a chair close to where he stood, sinking into it with the sort of languid grace which was now so familiar to her. No doubt of it, he was an arrogant, pompous man! – filled with a sense of his own superiority as he undoubtedly was.

The silence between them became an immense hush, falling like a blanket over everything as for one surprising interlude even the cicadas ceased their noise. Uncomfortable in the extreme, Helen looked uncertainly at the door leading into the room behind her, unable to make up her mind whether or not to make her departure, leaving her husband in sole possession of the patio. But she knew instinctively that he would follow her, so she remained where she was. As for Nick himself, he leant back in luxurious comfort against the cushions and it seemed that he was here for the rest of the night. Biting her lip in vexation, Helen left her chair and stood by the rail again. The hum of insects broke the silence, and the breeze blew a little cooler, tousling her hair. She felt her husband's eyes upon her, but did not turn.

Time passed and she became more uncomfortable, and more tired. What was this game he played? – some sort of mental torture? Not quite that, she owned, but that he was playing a game with her was most certainly the case. At last she made her decision, and went into the house. She had not been in her room for more than a few minutes when he appeared, entering almost noise-lessly, and closing the door softly behind him. Helen was brushing her hair and she continued to do so, neither turning her head nor speaking.

Her temper rose as through the mirror she saw him coming towards her. Fool that she was, denying herself the ability to speak, to tell him to go to his own room – and stay there!

"Put the brush down, Helen." The order came softly when, tightening her hands round the silver handle, it seemed she would resort to action seeing that she could not employ words. "Put it down, I say." No response from Helen. He said, even more softly, "Throw it at me and within seconds you'll be feeling it about your sides."

She did turn then, furious words springing to her lips, to be quelled at the last moment by the expression of sardonic expectancy on her husband's face. But she continued to gape at him, dark venom in her eyes. The brush was still held, and it was only the conviction that he made no idle threat that checked her from throwing it at his head. His dark eyes were fixed upon her face, but presently they were lowered to the brush. He told her again to put it down and when, quite unable to succumb meekly to his authoritative order, she ignored it, he covered the last small distance separating them in a couple of strides and, bending down, took the brush from her. But he had to do it by force, as she clung tightly to it in her obstinacy, and in a sudden spurt of temper he rapped her smartly across the knuckles with it. She flinched and touched her hand soothingly, tears starting to her eyes and an angry exclamation to her lips. This latter was stemmed, but fury raged within her. She would have to speak, she thought, but once again refrained on noting the gleam of amused waiting in his eyes.

So he was intent on forcing her to speak, was he? Helen's mouth took on a grim line as this idea occurred to her. He would have to try a great deal harder than this in order to break down her resistance!

But she was to have this resistance tried even further, because Nick had no intention of leaving her room. He lay comfortably in bed a few minutes later and waited for her to get undressed. For a long while she sat there, on the stool in front of the dressing-table; but the time dragged by and she found herself almost unable to keep her eyes open. She glanced at her watch, which was lying on the top of her jewel-box. Five minutes past one. Her glance flickered to her husband; he was on one elbow now, perusing a book of poems he had picked up from the table by the bed. Her blood boiled and nothing would have given her greater satisfaction than to snatch it from him and fling it away out of his reach.

At half past one he said, in that detestably quiet voice,

"Are you going to get undressed – or must I help you?"

She lowered her lashes, an idea having come to her. Just along the passage was a bedroom with a lock on the door. If she could reach it, enter, and then turn the key before Nick grasped her intention, then she would have thwarted him and, for good measure, have humiliated him into the bargain.

Picking up her dressing-gown with an air of meekness, she made as if to go to the bathroom, but with a lightning spring she was through the bedroom door and racing along the passage. Entering the room, she slammed the door and began fumbling with the key, trying to turn it. But it was stiff and stubborn and with an angry murmur of frustration she accepted that her plan had failed. Seconds later she stepped back swiftly; the door was swung open and Nick stood there, clad only in pyjama trousers, his long slender hands opening and closing as if they itched to do her an injury.

She faced him, white and taut as anger and fear battled for supremacy.

"What's the idea?" he snarled in low vibrating tones. "Have you forgotten the bargain you made?" No answer from Helen. "You made it and by God you'll keep it!" And before she could even hope to make a move to avoid him Helen found herself swept into his arms and, unwilling to lose her dignity entirely, she lay passive as he carried her back to the room from which she had tried to escape. "Yes, you'll keep your bargain – now and for always!" Nick's dark face swam above her for one fleeting second before his lips crushed hers, crushed them ruthlessly and possessively, as her body was crushed against the sinewed hardness of his. Fury and passion and the pagan desire for mastery all combined to heighten his emotions and she was almost swooning by the time he had released her. "Remain dumb if you want," he told her in a throaty bass tone, "but you'll remain obedient also!"

CHAPTER SIX

OVER a week had elapsed since Helen's firm declaration that she would speak to Nick only when he apologized for saying that she had looked like a common fishwife. The war was really on, with Nick clearly disinclined to communicate with her, but insisting on his rights and reminding her – each time she tried to resist him – that he meant to force her to honour her side of the bargain they had made.

"The servants must by now have noticed that you're not speaking to me," he told her one day when on Helen having taken a stroll into the grounds he came up to her in a quiet secluded spot. "If it comes to my ears that gossip is going on then I warn you, Helen, you'll be sorry for yourself." That was all; she glared at him and turned away, while Nick himself strode off in the direction of the house. A few minutes later Julia appeared carrying an airmail letter which she gave to Helen.

"From England, Mrs. Nikolas. You will be glad to have news from your family, yes?"

"Yes, Julia, I will. Thank you."

"You would like a drink?" inquired Julia. "It is very hot today and I can bring you out some lemonade which I make myself."

"That will be nice," smiled Helen, requesting that a couple of ice cubes be included. "I'll be here, on this seat."

"Under the tree? That is a cool place to sit, Mrs. Nikolas."

The letter was from her mother and Helen opened it with a tiny sigh. She would have liked to have had a really close relationship with her mother, but this had somehow never been possible. Whose fault it was Helen did not know; all she did know was that she had been robbed of something vitally important in her life. She had an abundance of love to give ... and there had never been anyone to give it to.

"I bring your drink, Mrs. Nikolas."

"Thank you, Julia." Helen took the glass from the tray and put it down on the seat beside her, returning her attention to the letter as soon as Julia had gone.

The contents had brought her mixed feelings – very mixed feelings, since her mother wanted to come over with Harold for a fortnight's holiday.

What could she reply? There was no feasible excuse for not having them, but on the other hand, how could she have visitors while this impossible situation existed between her husband and herself?

At lunch time she passed the letter to him across the table, flushing slightly as, taking it from her, he allowed his amused gaze to linger on her while at the same time making that characteristic lift to his brows. She set her teeth and nothing would have satisfied her more than to fling some scathing remark at him.

"You're in a mess, aren't you?" he said in some amusement when, on having read through the letter, he offered it back to her. "You'll either have to break your silence or tell them they can't come." His lips twitched as Helen made a palpable attempt at indifference without the necessity of speaking a word. "Incidentally," he remarked, helping himself to salad from a dish in the centre of the table, "you've given me quite a surprise by the length of time you've been able to maintain a silence. Never could I have believed it possible for a woman to hold her tongue for so long a period. I believe you're unique."

She sent him a speaking glance and cut the bread on her side plate with so much force that she half expected to see the plate itself come apart. The knife clattered down and again she was treated to an amused glance accompanied by that infuriating lift of his brows. Why did he have so many irritating mannerisms! Her inner fury became more and more manifest as the meal proceeded and now the humorous gleam in his eyes was traded for one of contempt, the amused quirk of his mouth replaced by a sneer.

"I'm fast reaching the point where I shall be driven to taking you in hand," he quietly informed her, and she jerked to attention, her wide eyes enquiring but retaining their expression of angry hauteur for all that. Her husband nodded, silently answering her question, but added, "Yes, my girl, I'm beginning to think that chastisement is the only remedy for a mulish, intractable wife."

He was goading her so that she would speak, but difficult though her silence was to maintain, she would not afford him the satisfaction of forcing her to surrender. Yet deep down inside her she had to admit that the whole situation had long since become absurd. Her declaration had been made on angry impulse and had she stopped to think before making it she would of course have held her tongue, for she knew Nick well enough to be sure that he would never lower his pride sufficiently to make her an apology. In any case, he himself did not consider an apology was required since he had meant what he said.

It was much later, when she was returning from a stroll round the town, that he re-introduced the subject of her mother's visit, asking if she had made up her mind about it, as he wanted to know whether or not she and her husband would be coming. He spoke conversationally, and with a pleasant edge to his voice – just as if there were no disunity between them, she thought. Just as if she would reply naturally to his question. Instead, she gave him an insolent glance and brushed past him, making her way to her bedroom, her head in the air. He followed, his footsteps silent on the thick carpet, and he was in the room and closing the door before she realized he was there at all. Turning, she faced him, trying to ignore the fact that her heart was pounding uncomfortably, trying to convince herself that she was *not* trembling with apprehension. But there was no mistaking that expression; she had seen it before. It was a mask of sheer undiluted fury displayed by the smouldering embers lying deep in those black eyes, the rhythmic throb of a muscle in his throat, the tight line of his mouth . . . ruthless and cruel. His voice when he spoke was soft, but sibilant . . . like the low warning hiss of a snake about to strike. Standing her ground with difficulty, Helen had sent him an enquiring look, at the same time unconsciously pushing the palms of her hands against the sides of her dress, for they were clammy with perspiration that had appeared quite suddenly.

"I warned you," he reminded her, "and you've chosen to disregard that warning –" With a couple of strides he dispensed with the distance separating them and although she made a swift step backwards she was seized by the wrist and jerked forward again, coming up against that iron-hard body with a jerk. With one hand he held her wrist while with the other he took hold of her hair and tugged it so that her face was upturned to his. She almost cried out with the pain, but managed to bite back the exclamation just in time. "And now," he snarled close to her face, "do I give you a damned good box on the ears or will you have it where it doesn't show?"

She did utter a gasp then, for never had she really believed he would resort to physical violence. He seemed too aloof and reserved, too much the gentleman to lay a hand on a woman. But it seemed that she was wrong, for there was no doubt whatsoever in her mind that he meant what he said. He spoke again, repeating his question; she was in a quandary, since if she still refused to speak he would give her the treatment which in his opinion fitted her crime.

"Speak!" he thundered, his fury breaking all bonds now. "Speak – and say how you will have it!" And without waiting for her to make up her mind he shook her unmercifully, till her hair was falling all over her face. Then he gathered it into his hand again and her head was once more jerked back, a sharp pain shooting through it – a pain that brought tears springing to her eyes.

Stubbornly she held her silence, only to be viciously shaken again. And when it seemed that he actually would strike her she could do nothing else than allow the cry to escape her.

"Don't you dare! I – I shall retaliate – and – and hit you back!"

"So. . . ." Triumph came slowly to his hard features; the dark eyes flickered over her flushed face and in them

101

she noted the arrogant gleam. Black rage consumed her, bringing tears to her lashes. "I hadn't deliberately meant to bend you, Helen, but you drove me. No woman gives me the kind of look which you gave me just now and gets away with it. Love I have never expected from you, but respect I demand." He paused, affording her time to speak; she muttered under her breath something about his remark on love, adding that it was hate she felt for him, venomous hate. He merely lifted the corner of his mouth in a gesture of amusement, but there was not a vestige of humour in his voice as he continued, "I ought to force an apology from you, but I can see that you're in a mood to keep this quarrel going, so I'll leave it for the present –"

"You've no option," she flashed. "I would never apologize – never!"

An ugly glint in his eye and a suddening compression of his mouth and then,

"Be careful, Helen. You've just been brought to your knees, but –"

"Oh," she seethed, glaring viciously at him, "how dare you put it like that!"

"–it doesn't appear to have taught you a lesson," he continued, ignoring the interruption. He stood now with his back to the open window, a formidable figure but a noble one, whose every body line spelled arrogance – the set of his head on broad straight shoulders, the facial contours that reminded Helen of the sculptures of the ancient Greeks, and even the spare and angular frame with its hidden strength and muscle. Helen's angry eyes went past him to the beautiful garden scene beyond, where a symphony of colour was created by the numerous flowering trees and shrubs, and the exotic flowers which sprayed the fresh sweet air with their exotic scents, scents that mingled intoxicatingly with that of the pines growing above the undulating grassy slopes forming the mountain foothills. Cicadas whirred on this still scented air and peace reigned over the whole idyllic scene – so at variance with the atmosphere pervading the room, an atmosphere dominated by hate on the one hand and arrogance on the other as the two occupants gazed at one another – Helen's mouth tight, Nick's twisted by a hint of sardonic amusement which brought to Helen a feeling of inferiority that served only to increase her fury, and her hatred for her husband.

After standing there for what seemed an interminable time, Nick crossed the room and, flicking her cheek with an arrogant finger, he gave her a final warning,

"Take care, Helen. Desist from playing with fire, for believe me, if you don't, you're going to get burned . . . badly." And without affording her the opportunity of producing a retort he continued across the room and went out, closing the door softly behind him.

Helen stared at it, her whole body affected by the conflagration within her. The humiliation through which she had passed filled her mind and the hatred she felt for her husband increased. She naturally thought of Paul, and the reason for her marriage. Gritting her teeth, she once again cursed herself for choosing marriage as the remedy to use as a deterrent against Paul's optimism. Looking back Helen realized that it had been Paul's words that had been of paramount importance in guiding her towards the disastrous step she had so foolishly taken, he had said that she would marry him eventually, and gone on to say,

"You're free. If you were married it might be different; the problem would be greater, the obstacles more formidable. But as it is, with your being totally unhampered, the way won't be too difficult."

And in order to make the way too difficult, she had gone to the lengths of marriage with this detestable foreigner. She must have been out of her mind! But at the time there did exist an urgency about the whole siuation, with Paul threatening to disclose the name of the girl with whom he had fallen in love, and poor Fran passing through a period of acute misery and uncertainty. To Helen her own marriage seemed to provide the remedy and the result was that she had gone headlong into it.

And now there was no escape, for much as she would like to leave her husband she was bound to him by the fact that her conscious and sense of honour forbade the breaking of the contract she had so readily made with Nick at the time. Yes, she was bound . . . by these fetters imposed by conscience and honour, fetters that had become steeped in hate.

Although she was now on speaking terms with Nick she spoke only when necessary, and the situation became such that a rift yawned between them that would – in Helen's opinion – never be bridged. However, with the visit of her mother and Harold open hostility had to be avoided, and the day before they were expected Helen mentioned this to her husband. They were sunbathing on the lawn, Nick having come from the swimming-pool just a few minutes previously. That he should have chosen to come and occupy a place close to where she was lying had surprised her, since he had a vast area from which to choose. At her rather halting but icy words he turned his head towards her, narrowing his eyes against the sun.

"You want me to put on the pretence of being a loving husband, is that what you're trying to tell me?"

She said, an edge of irritation to her voice,

"There's no need to be sarcastic. I'm making a reasonable request, as I don't want my mother – and especially my stepfather – to know what a mess I've made of my life." Not a tactful approach when asking a favour; Helen realized this but, unfortunately, a little late.

"A mess?" he repeated, a twist of anger in his tone. "So you're already regretting your bargain?"

"Naturally I'm regretting it, after what has just happened."

"Rather late, don't you think?"

"I'm not blaming you –"

"That's generous," with icy sarcasm and a contemptuous flicker of his eyes over her near naked body. "Am I supposed to be grateful for this?"

Helen's small hands clenched at her sides.

"Can we keep to the question of Mother's visit?" she asked, having the greatest difficulty with her temper.

Her husband lifted a brown hand to stifle a yawn.

"It was you who deviated from it," he quietly reminded her, "by informing me that you had made a mess of your life by marrying me."

Her silence was an acknowledgement of the truth of this, and Nick continued by pointing out the numerous advantages which had gone with the marriage. She was now a woman of position who shared the wealth of her husband. He had denied her nothing that money could buy, nor would he ever do so. He had kept his part of the bargain to the letter; he expected her to do the same.

"I've no intention of doing anything else," she told him stiffly. "I've sold myself and I shall abide by what I've done." Something in her tone brought a frown of puzzlement to her husband's forehead and he asked softly, after a strange little pause,

"Just why did you decide to marry me – after having been so emphatic in your refusal?"

Swiftly she twisted her neck, so that her expressive eyes would not reveal anything which might arouse his suspicions. In reply to his initial question as to why she had decided to accept his offer she had lied and said that, after all, she had been tempted by his wealth and position; this answer had satisfied him, and she now repeated it, but still not daring to meet his gaze.

"You know very well why – for money and security."

"Look at me," he commanded gently after a small tense moment of silence. "I said . . . look at me."

Another silence and then she turned, half twisting her body so that she faced him. But her lashes fluttered down over her eyes and she was told again to look at him. At length she obeyed, her eyes meeting his. The lean dark face was inscrutable; the steely intentness of his gaze told her nothing. The expressionless tones of his voice were equally uncommunicative, and yet she felt disturbed by them.

"For money and security . . .?" He saw her nod – an urgent gesture which served to make his frown lines go a little deeper. "I seem to recall remarking on our honesty with one another," he continued thoughtfully, "a circumstance that should go far to ensuring a smooth path." His dark eyes flickered over her face. "Our path should by rights have been smooth, Helen, but it has turned out to be very far from that. Are you quite sure you were honest with me – that your reason for marrying me really was for the security and wealth it would bring to you?"

"Of course. Why should you think otherwise?" She was totally unaware of the note of urgency in her voice, but it did not escape her husband, whose eyes narrowed – and this time it was not against the fierce rays of the sun.

"If, then, you have been fully honest with me, and have in fact married me for the reasons stated, why are you now regretting the marriage?" Logical the question, and Helen had the grace to blush. But she could find no reasonable answer to offer and she had to fall silent – a sign of guilt in itself, and she sent up a little prayer that Nick would never learn of the real reason for her decision to accept his offer of marriage. "Your silence is, quite naturally, causing me to be in some doubt about your assertions," he added quietly when, after he had slanted her a glance of enquiry, she merely shook her head, denoting her inability to produce any verbal reply to his question. "If there was another – altogether different reason – then I am interested to hear about it."

She shrugged with well-feigned carelessness.

"I don't understand you, Nick. I've told you why I married you –" She spread her hands in another little piece of acting. "What else do you want me to say?"

"We'll leave the matter," he said, but Helen was faintly troubled by the half-shrewd inflection that fringed his voice. If by some unforeseen chance he should ever discover the truth he would without doubt recall this conversation, and her evasion of his pointed questions.

She thought of Paul's threat to follow her and for a moment real fear possessed her. But on recalling the contents of Fran's last letter Helen rather thought that the couple were getting along all right. At least Fran had made no mention at all of any unhappiness existing between Paul and herself. So it seemed unlikely that Nick would in fact ever discover the truth, and after convincing herself of this Helen found no difficulty at all in shrugging away her misgivings.

After deciding to let the subject drop Nick himself reintroduced the question of the visit of Helen's mother and her husband. He had never asked her anything about her life before she took the post in Athens, but now he did put forward a few queries and these Helen answered at once, thankful for the change of topic.

"And you want your parents to see a happy glowing daughter, adored by her husband?" He asked the question as she ceased speaking and the accents of sardonic amusement were very plain indeed. She flushed with anger and her lovely eyes sparkled. Nick leant on one elbow and looked at her with undisguised admiration as he allowed his glance to rove her face and the beautiful curves of her shoulders and neck and slender brown body.

"All I want is for you to act in a way that will not cause me any embarrassment."

"And you, my dear," he queried, "will you also play the game convincingly?"

"Of course."

"I'm to hear you call me darling, am I?" His gathering amusement became clear in his expression. He received a kindling look from his wife and the acid retort,

"We have no need to go quite as far as that!"

"No? Then how far must we go?"

She gave a deep sigh of exasperation.

"We need only be civil to one another," she told him at last, and he actually gave a gust of laughter.

"Civil? That shouldn't be too difficult, should it?"

"I just want you to be a little less aloof."

"Am I aloof?" He seemed surprised. But then he said, as if the thought had just occurred to him, "What else do you expect me to be, when you yourself remain dumb?"

"I'm on speaking terms with you now," she reminded him, quite unnecessarily, she realized, and glanced away to hide her embarrassment when again he laughed.

"This conversation's becoming absurd. So you want me to display a little affection, is that it?"

"If it isn't too much trouble."

He shook his head.

"No trouble at all. I do happen to have had a great deal of experience," he could not help adding, as if deliberately to rile her.

"No doubt you have," was her cool response. "I am not interested, though, in your dissolute past."

"A nice thrust," he laughed, and added, "If you continue in this irascible, shrewish way I shall begin to regret having given up my dissolute past, as you term it."

"You could go back."

His eyes glinted at this.

109

"I've warned you, Helen, to be careful. Try my patience too far and by heaven I'll leave you smarting for a week!"

Swift rosy colour flooded her cheeks, and she opened her mouth to flash him a venomous retort, but she closed it again, deep trepidation stealing over her at his expression. It told her very plainly that it would take very little provocation on her part for his threat to be carried out.

Much as it went against the grain she spoke in a subdued tone when presently she said,

"So you're agreeable to our – er – being more friendly – just while the visit lasts?"

"We'll drop hostilities, yes."

"Thank you." A small pause and then, "You will meet them at the airport?"

"Naturally."

"Thank you," she said again, and lapsed into silence.

There was no eager expectancy attached to the visit as far as Helen was concerned, and once again she felt she had been robbed of something vitally important in her life. However, she was glad of the visit since it must surely ease the situation between Nick and herself, a situation that had begun on his seeing her sitting there chatting to John. Before then life had been drifting along pleasant lines and Helen knew that had she been able to forget that her husband's sole interest in her was desire then she could actually have been happy. What this meant basically she had never asked herself; all she did know was that she had on occasions experienced the strangest emotions when with Nick, and that on one particular occasion when he had said "my Helen" she had wished it

110

could have been "my love". Significant, surely?

But now all that Helen felt for him was hatred – hatred for the way he tyrannised over her, mastering her to the point where she was deeply affected by humility. She hated him for the hold he had on her even though it was part of the bargain into which she had entered with eyes wide open; she hated him for his sarcasm and mockery and that infuriating air of superiority he seemed always to carry. Most of all she hated him for the fear that he could put into her by his temper and his threats.

He turned his head as if suddenly aware of the fact that she was focusing all her attention on him. She coloured and lowered her lashes, aware of his strange expression, and of his interest; this latter reminded her of the interest he had shown when they were on holiday in Istanbul.

"You're the most beautiful woman I have ever seen," he murmured unexpectedly, and a frown disturbed the serenity that had settled on her brow.

"You've said that before," she reminded him.

"And I shall say it again – many times," he assured her with a sudden smile. "What amazes me is why you were never caught before."

"Caught?" she repeated, her frown deepening.

"A mere figure of speech, my dear." Turning on to his side, he perplexedly shook his head. "You must have had admirers by the dozen." A question; she replied to it coolly, and truthfully.

"Not dozens. These days men give their attention to those women whom they term good sports."

His firm lips twitched.

"That's what you call them in your country?"

"And so," she went on ignoring this, "I have never been troubled by men very much." Her thoughts naturally went to Paul and she wondered even yet again what it was that had come to them. Some transient thing, obviously, since she now felt nothing – no emotion whatsoever. She surmised he was the same, having now settled down happily with Fran. She sincerely hoped so, but recalling just how they were both affected by one another she did sometimes wonder what would have been the result had Paul been free at the time they had met.

"Can you tell me truthfully that you've never been in love?" The harsh note creeping into his voice as this question was put brought to Helen's mind her previous conviction that in jealousy he would be a fiend.

"I haven't ever been in love," she replied, but for some reason she lowered her lashes, as even now she found it impossible to analyse the feeling she had had for Fran's fiancé.

And when at length she looked at Nick she saw that his eyes had narrowed to mere slits, and that his mouth was tightly compressed. For some inexplicable reason a shiver passed through her and for the rest of the day a heavy weight of foreboding lay ominously upon her.

CHAPTER SEVEN

HELEN had often wondered what her mother thought of her marriage to a Greek, but apart from her initial surprise Mrs. Lynch had shown very little interest. Wrapped up as she was in her husband, she never had much time for anyone else. She had shown no curiosity at the haste with which the marriage had taken place, had never stopped to wonder if the circumstances might not be quite right.

But she now knew that something had been amiss, and the moment she found herself alone with her daughter she set her heart thudding by mentioning Paul, saying that he had called several times, wanting to know if Helen was still living with her husband.

"He seemed to think you'd have left him before now," continued Mrs. Lynch, even in this situation evincing very little emotion of any kind. "I did begin to wonder, Helen, if there had been something between you and Paul – before his marriage, of course?"

White and tense, Helen asked,

"When was the last time he visited you, Mother?"

"Only the day before we came away. We've had two days in Athens, as you know, so it would be –" She stopped a second to think. "Tuesday – yes, it was; Tuesday evening. Harold was so curious, asking him what it was all about. You know how Harold is, don't you, dear? He hates anything underhand or – er – sordid."

A glint entered Helen's eyes at this, but she made no comment on it. She was far more interested in Paul's visits than in the interpretation her stepfather might put on them.

"What did Paul come for? He knew you were coming to me for a holiday?" she added with a sudden frown.

"Yes, of course. I had told him when he came to visit us on a previous occasion. On Tuesday he asked me to give you a letter, saying he could not post one to you as

113

your husband might get hold of it."

"A letter? You have it handy." Helen's eyes went to the large suitcase which she herself had carried up a few moments ago when taking her mother to the lovely bedroom overlooking the *perivoli* at the back of the villa.

"It's in my handbag." She opened the bag and extracted the letter. And now she did betray a modicum of curiosity. "Paul seemed most unhappy, and yet at the same time I felt that he was angry too – angry with you."

Extending a hand, Helen took the letter, staring down at the handwriting, a strange sense of foreboding taking possession of her. She knew instinctively that Paul was to cause her more trouble yet, and the knowledge sent a quiver of trepidation running along her spine; and on her lips was a little prayer that her husband would never learn of her deceit when she had given him the reason for accepting his offer of marriage.

"Thank you." Helen murmured the two brief words and put the letter into the pocket of her dress.

"Was there something between you?" asked her mother outright at last.

"I never met Paul until after his engagement to Fran," she answered, looking straight at her. "How could there have been anything between us?"

"I must admit that I was surprised at your decision to move to Birmingham, and then to get married – Oh, I know you told us that Nick was known to you and that you and he had been about together, but when you came home you didn't seem to me to be in love. And you never had a letter from Nick while you were with us."

Helen licked her lips, wondering what to say. However, she was destined not to say anything at present be-

114

cause at that moment the door swung inwards and her stepfather appeared, his fair hair waved as if by his own hand with electric tongs, his eyes appearing to be paler and more expressionless than ever, his chin more weak and receding. Lord, what did her mother see in the dandy? Helen could not help making a comparison – and a surge of pride swept through her as she pictured the scene when Harold and Nick had greeted one another at the airport less than an hour ago. Towering above Harold, Nick had appeared as a feudal lord looking down with unveiled contempt at his surf. The contempt could not be suppressed; Helen saw this at once. But Harold was too dim to notice. He had tilted his head as his limp hand was taken, and, seeing him wince, Helen strongly suspected her husband of deliberately gripping it hard.

Revolted now at the appearance of Harold, Helen chided herself for making a comparison at all. There really was none, for how could the superlative be compared with the inferior?

"I'm glad I've got this opportunity of speaking to you alone," he began without preamble. "Your mother doesn't like to accept the obvious – but then she's your doting parent and I'm not." He crossed the room with mincing steps and stood with his back to the dressing-table trying to look stern. Serious as was the position, and troubled as she was by the information imparted by her mother, Helen had the greatest difficulty in suppressing the laughter that fought for release. His pale mean eyes surveyed her with an expression of acute disdain. "As you know, Helen, I am decidedly against the abandonment of the moral code that is taking place today. And although you might resent my interference I feel it's my duty to in-form you of my strong disapproval regarding your relationship with your best friend's husband. You ought not to be receiving letters from him –" He stopped and lifted a thin white finger. "Secretly!"

Going pale with anger, Helen just stood there, aware of her mother's discomfort as she stared from one to the other. At length she spoke, and just as Helen expected she supported her husband.

"Harold's right, dear. You shouldn't be receiving letters from Paul. There must be something between you, as dear Harold maintained after Paul's first visit to us. Because if there's nothing then why should he have thought that you might have left your husband? This is what troubled Harold."

How she kept her temper Helen would never know. It was probably the subconscious fear that all would be revealed to Nick were she to quarrel with her stepfather. But she was already regretting having him here. She could have made some excuse, she thought, but at the time she had never for one moment suspected that she would find herself in a position such as this.

"I do realize how Harold feels, Mother," she said at last, with commendable restraint, "but my affairs are my own, and therefore his – er – concern is unnecessary." Transferring her gaze, she looked at him. "You really have no need to worry, Harold, I'm not in the least interested in Fran's husband."

"Your mother seems to think that you and he might have fallen in love –"

"No such thing!"

"Well, it was most strange that you should go off to Birmingham like that."

116

"It would appear that you and Mother have been discussing me at some length," with a tart edge to her voice despite her reluctance to create any unpleasantness between Harold and herself.

"Naturally we have. This Greek had never been mentioned by you, and yet the next thing we knew you were marrying him."

Helen's eyes kindled at the manner in which he referred to Nick, but once again she managed to control her temper.

"As Mother knows, Nick and I had met when I was working in Athens."

"You never mentioned him in any of your letters, though," intervened her mother as if deciding she must put in another word of support for her husband. "A girl in love is usually expansive about her young man."

"I didn't know that Nick wanted to marry me at that time. It wasn't until I came home that he – he missed me." She turned away as she spoke, because although no deliberate lie was involved she was in fact deceiving her mother, and in consequence a hint of guilty colour tinged her cheeks.

"It's my opinion," cut in Harold with a frown, "that you and Paul were having an affair, right under your friend's nose, and that the affair is by no means at an end."

Helen gritted her teeth, and it did seem that her temper would prevail over her efforts at calm. The man spoke in so absurd a manner, though, that she realized he hadn't even given a thought to what he said. For had she and Paul been having an affair before either of them was married, then they would obviously have married each

117

other, and not someone else.

At last she said, looking straight at him,

"Can we let this matter drop, Harold? As I've said, my affairs are my own and need not trouble you. We all want this to be a pleasant stay, and so perhaps we can forget this little interview and start from now?"

"You always did have a clever way of evading things unpleasant," he said, reluctant to put an end to the conversation before discovering more. "There's a mystery, Helen, and your mother and father are those in whom you should confide."

At this she couldn't help saying, in a voice that quivered slightly,

"But you're not my father, Harold."

"He's taken his place, though," began her mother, when a lift of Helen's hand silenced her.

"No one can take his place." She was still pale, and her hands felt clammy, because she had been clenching them, quite unconsciously. "I want no more said on this matter –" Her glance went from one to the other. "Is that understood?"

"Well. . . ." Her mother shook her head. "Harold said he intended to get to the bottom of the matter. After all, Helen dear, Paul has written secretly. If everything were open and above board then why couldn't he have sent the letter by post? He said when he gave it to me that he hadn't communicated with you because of his fear that your husband would get hold of the letters."

"What should he be writing that your husband couldn't see?" asked Harold accusingly, and now Helen's temper broke the rein she had held upon it.

"Mind your own business! I refuse to be questioned

like this! The fact that you're Mother's husband doesn't entitle you to interfere in my affairs. I've tried to keep my patience, but it's now becoming difficult."

"Hush, dear," interrupted her mother soothingly. "It's just that Harold is anxious about you."

"I was watching you closely when we arrived," said Harold, apparently unperturbed by Helen's outburst. "And I said to your mother afterwards that you are definitely not in love with your husband."

"How very observant! I must correct you, though. I am in love with my husband." This was a deliberate lie and she lowered her head, angry that the necessary lie had been forced from her by a man to whom she owed nothing.

"You didn't act as if you were," her mother murmured, aware now that a quarrel was brewing. "You did seem cool with him, dear."

Helen looked at her.

"Do you expect me to be demonstrative in public! "

"Don't shout," chided Mrs. Lynch, a pained expression settling on her face. "If things are going to be as unpleasant as this then I shall regret coming to see you."

Helen sighed. What a disastrous start they had made! And yet she could not in any way blame herself, but to some extent she blamed her mother, who should have put her husband in his place, firmly letting him know that he had no right at all to interest himself in his stepdaughter's affairs.

"I'd better leave you," said Helen at last, with another sigh. "Nick's ordered tea for you; it will be ready in about half an hour."

"Thank you." Her mother hesitated, glancing at her husband. "Perhaps we ought not to bother our heads about Helen," she told him. "After all, she's been independent for a long time now."

"I was merely trying to guide her on the right path," rather sulkily from Harold. "She's asking for trouble in being underhand with her husband."

Although seething inwardly Helen managed to suppress the flare of anger that threatened and, diplomatically, she said, in a quiet tone of reserve,

"I'll see you in about half an hour. Tea will be served on the front patio." And with that she left the room, her head in the air and a glint in her eye as she walked past her stepfather.

Once in her own room she slit the envelope of Paul's letter and read:

"My dear Helen,

I could not resist seizing this opportunity of communicating with you. Your mother will have told you of my several calls at her home, and these were made because I know instinctively that the day is near when you will leave the husband you married in such haste – married with the absurd idea that it would put an end to what you felt must develop into an affair between you and me. But, Helen, it wouldn't have been an affair, because I wanted to marry you, as you well knew. I am not remaining with Fran, and it seems that fate is on my side because she has lost the baby. When she is fully recovered from her disappointment I shall be frank with her and tell her that you and I fell in love.

I expect by now you are bitterly regretting your foolishness and wishing you were with me. If you feel as I feel then I pity you, for I am the most unhappy man on earth. Please write to me, Helen. You can send letters to the office and so Fran will never know about them. When I have straightened out things with her I shall make it my business to come over to see you and we can then make our plans for the future.

My love to you always,
Paul."

The paper shook in Helen's hand. But for the moment all that stood out was the fact that Fran had lost the child. Had she not done so then Helen felt convinced that Paul would have had so much love for it that he could not for one moment have considered leaving it.

But the child – the link that surely would have kept Paul at Fran's side – was lost, and now it seemed that Paul considered himself free. Fate was on his side, he had said. How could he be so heartless? Sickened, Helen whispered quiveringly,

"If you had an ounce of common sense you'd realize that no girl in her right mind would marry a man so utterly without feeling as you."

What then began to trouble Helen was his statement about coming over here to see her. He seemed unable to grasp the fact that she definitely did not want him, and Helen saw that the only thing to do would be for *her* to go to England and see *him*. She could then convince him once and for all that she had no intention of having anything whatever to do with him.

But how was she to visit England? There was no excuse which she could think up. In any case, should she have been able to do so it was more than likely that Nick would immediately offer to accompany her.

As the minutes passed a sort of despairing panic seized her, for it did seem that sooner or later Nick was going to learn the real reason for her marrying him. She shivered, dread engulfing her as she recalled even yet again her previous conviction that in jealousy her husband would be a fiend. There had also been his statement that they had both been honest with one another, a circumstance that should have – so he said – made their path smooth. Their path had not been smooth and already a hint of suspicion had entered her husband's mind.

At last she put the letter in a drawer and went downstairs to where Nick was standing on the edge of the lawn, staring down at the flowers in the border edging it. Glancing up as she came to join him, he smiled amusedly and said,

"That fellow gets worse. I don't recall him being quite so foppish – but then I didn't see much of him at the wedding. We rushed it, rather." A small pause and then, "Where on earth did your mother find him?"

Helen shrugged.

"Heaven knows. She loves him, though, so I suppose that's all that matters. They're very happy together."

"What was your father like?" He examined her features as the question was phrased; she knew he was taking in the strong character lines of her face.

"Not like Harold, certainly."

"That's evident." The dark eyes still examined. "I asked you what he was like."

"Tall and strong in build. A thoughtful man, intelligent. . . ." Helen trailed off, shrugging her shoulders. "He was a man," was the simple addition she made, and

122

her husband nodded his head a little pensively.

"What, then, possessed your mother to marry a popinjay like that?"

"Some women are unpredictable in their actions."

He smiled at this.

"Some?" he repeated. "Most, I have found."

"Have it your own way, Nick. I'm in no mood for an argument."

He raised his brows.

"You're not too happy, apparently? Something wrong?"

Swiftly she shook her head.

"No, of course not. What could be wrong?"

"You've a little too much colour. I believe you've been in a temper?"

Involuntarily she gave a sigh of impatience.

"Please don't keep on," she begged. "In any case, it's all right now."

"That's cryptic. You've got me curious."

"If you must know, I did have a few words – unpleasant words – with Harold. He tried to interfere in something that wasn't any of his business."

Puzzled, Nick frowned at her.

"Can't I know what it was all about?" he asked, and Helen immediately shook her head.

"It was a private matter –"

"But Harold didn't consider it so?"

Another impatient sigh escaped her; she seemed to be becoming involved and it was imperative that she extricate herself without leaving suspicion in her husband's mind.

"He likes to think he's taken Father's place. I told him

that he could never do that."

Nick's eyes had narrowed a little.

"Just what are you keeping from me, Helen?" he inquired in a very soft tone.

She paled somewhat but managed not to falter as she replied,

"It's nothing important, Nick —"

"In that case, why aren't you being open about it?"

"Because it doesn't concern you," she lied, averting her head.

"I don't like secrets, Helen."

"For heaven's sake, let it drop!" she cried fiercely. "Have you no secrets which you keep from me?"

His dark eyes glittered strangely at this sudden outburst, an outburst that Helen knew full well must only give an added element of mystery to the situation, but her nerves were affected by her husband's questioning and also by the nagging conviction that if she did not manage somehow to get to England then Paul would come here and cause her a great deal of trouble.

"Guilt," he observed softly after a while, "is written all over your face."

"You have a vivid imagination!"

"And you an uncontrollable temper," he countered, diverted by her anger, and puzzled by it too.

"I wouldn't have lost it if you'd let the matter drop, as I asked you to!" Her voice was raised, and it was at this particular moment that her stepfather happened to come from the house on to the lawn. And instead of applying tact and good manners he did no more than come swiftly towards them and ask if anything was wrong.

"You sounded as if you were quarrelling," he added,

and an awful silence followed as Nick, drawing himself up to his full forbidding height, stared glintingly down at the insignificant figure of Harold. Swiftly Helen said,

"Nick's in one of his teasing moods, and I was protesting. But we were certainly not quarrelling. We never do –" She looked up at Nick and her glance was a miracle of feigned tenderness which actually made her husband give a slight start. "Do we, darling?" Her voice and her manner were pleading and after the merest hesitation he responded with,

"Of course not, my love." And to Harold he said, "Take no notice of Helen and me; we often play this sort of game."

"Indeed?" with a look from one to the other. "It did seem, though, that Helen was. . . ." He allowed his thin reedy voice to trail away as Nick held his gaze. "I'm sorry," he muttered presently, "my mistake."

Tea was an ordeal, with Nick, soon losing patience with the inane conversation taking place betweeen Harold and his wife, falling silent, and Helen acutely conscious of a coolness existing between herself and the visitors.

"How on earth are we to get through the next fortnight?" she had to ask later when she and Nick happened to find themselves alone for a while. "I ought not to have had them. It isn't as if I've ever got on with my stepfather."

Nick appeared ready to say something, but changed his mind. Helen sensed that he had been on the verge of re-opening the subject they had been engaged in earlier, but that he had decided to leave it in abeyance for the time being.

"We shall have to make them comfortable," he said at

length, "if only for the sake of good manners. Perhaps we can persuade them to go off on their own now and then, while on other occasions we shall have to play the part of good hosts and entertain them."

Suddenly she was all apology, knowing just how Nick must be feeling – bored to distraction by having to endure the company of a man like Harold Lynch who had no intelligent conversation, and in addition was not a good listener. He just had to talk – about anything that came into his head.

"I'm sorry, Nick," she murmured. "I ought to have given the matter a little more thought before agreeing that they should visit us."

He seemed to understand how awkward it was for her and his voice was soft as he told her not to worry unduly as a fortnight was not an eternity.

"You couldn't have put them off in any case," he added. "There was no excuse you could have made for doing so."

"No, I suppose not," she agreed flatly. "All the same, I shall be counting the days until their visit is at an end." She and Nick were in the sitting-room, standing by the open window, and from the garden the breeze drifted in, perfumed by the flowers and the tall pines swaying on the hillside. Oleanders in great clusters nodded and added their exotic scent to the air; plane trees formed a backcloth to the vivid sub-tropical colour which gave the scene its breathtaking beauty. And quietness prevailed, with only the murmur of busy insects invading it; over all was an atmosphere of warm simplicity in spite of the magnificence of the garden layout. The sun was dropping behind the hills, leaving a symphony of crimson and gold streaking across the sky.

The combination of all these evoked a strange emotion in Helen and peace enclosed her so that the presence of her unwanted visitors no longer shadowed her horizon. She was aware only of another presence, that of her husband, eclipsing everything that was unpleasant. His keen dark eyes were upon her – in admiration. Her mouth quivered as nerves tingled; she desired that he kiss her . . . and he did.

"My God, but you're beautiful!" His lips possessed once more, and even yet again. "Don't tempt me, woman, for I'm only human!" But the words were a caress, the desire a compliment as high as any he could give. "Helen . . . my wife. . . ."

She clung to him, and closed her eyes tightly, for a deep hurt wrenched at her heartstrings, like the plucking of a merciless claw. "My wife. . . ." If only he would say, "My love. . . ."

The jerk of her heart and pulse, the increased tingling of nerves; the dawning perception of mind that Helen fiercely thrust away, the fear that slowly took possession – fear of the future and of unrequited love.

Yes, it was out at last. Perception refused any longer to be denied. Fool that she was! – falling in love with a man who had bought her in cold blood simply because he had failed to possess her in any other way. Marriage to her had been for him a necessity, the necessity of the flesh and nothing more. He had found that he could not do without her, and for the assuaging of his appetite he had given up his freedom.

Tears stung her eyes suddenly; she felt small and helpless and drained of spirit; a great shuddering sigh rose from the very depths of her so that her body quivered against the muscled hardness of his. He drew away, holding her at arms' length.

"Helen," he said in some concern, "what is it?"

Dumbly she shook her head. Pride fought for ascendency because she desired most urgently to conceal the truth from him. But her pride was unable to rise to it; it was as low as her spirits. Nick repeated his question, this time in commanding tones, and at last she said evasively,

"It's nothing, Nick. I'm just a little dejected, that's all."

He frowned at her, his expression stern.

"You're taking the matter far too seriously. They're here and we've to abide by it. Haven't I just said that it's not an eternity?"

She nodded, and on an uncontrollable impulse she did a most unexpected thing. She nestled close and rested her cheek against his breast. His arms went around her; she felt their warmth, and the caressing movement of his fingers. Deep contentment fell on her fleetingly, for this moment was heaven itself as she pretended that his love was all hers.

"No, Nick," she whispered in a muffled voice, "it's not an eternity."

A strange silence followed this sober agreement to what he had said. He seemed taken aback both by her action and the demure tone of her voice. But then he had rarely seen her in a docile mood. After a while he tilted up her face; she noted the perplexity in his eyes and fully understood the reason for it. What she did not understand was herself. This pretence, the futility of it . . . it was so unlike her to indulge in make-believe. But the magic and the miracle of nature as the lowering sun drenched the colour tapestry in a golden sheen, the silent tranquil atmosphere, the perfumes and the soft caressing breeze ... these had the most powerful effect on her, rendering her pliable and wanting to create a tender situation between her husband and herself. His hand was warm under her chin; his fingers moved, to curl around it and caress the softly-parted lips. Fire smouldered in the dark and pagan eyes ... the fire of ardour held in check. But there was no restraint in his kiss when presently his lips found hers; on the contrary, they demanded and possessed with all the arrogance of the god-king, Zeus himself. Triumph was displayed in their sensuous refusal to allow her to draw away when eventually she was breathless; it was only when desire was fully satisfied that she was freed.

"Oh. . . ." she gasped, taking in great gulps of air. "Nick . . . I couldn't breathe!"

A low laugh escaped him, the laugh of the victor. And yet, paradoxically, he said, his voice husky from ardour still unspent,

"I wonder if you know just how strong your attraction is? Never have I fallen under the spell of a woman as I've fallen under yours." He shook his head even while his lips caressed hers. "What it is I'll never know, but I'm beginning to think it's more than beauty."

Her heart leapt and her lovely eyes shone. Dared she venture to say, "It might be love?" Her lips parted as courage rose; a rebuff might be her reward, but she knew she had to take the risk.

"Nick . . . what you feel for me m-might –" She broke off abruptly as the door behind them opened, and her whole body sagged, for she knew instinctively that this lost moment would never return. With an almost baleful glance she took in the slim, tightly-clothed figure of Harold Lynch. Already Nick was drawing away, putting her from him, without haste or the loss of even a small measure of dignity.

Harold came forward, his mincing steps silent on the carpet.

"Do forgive me," he said with the kind of smile which made Helen want to wipe it from his face. "I seem to have entered at an inopportune moment. Do accept my apologies, won't you?"

CHAPTER EIGHT

OVER a week had elapsed, the longest week Helen had ever known, but yet a period when she came closer to her husband than she would ever have believed possible. After the fire and storm of their earlier relationship the quiet and tranquil atmosphere was like sweet balm to her heart, while to her husband it seemed to bring an equal measure of contentment and pleasure. He teased where once he had sneered, smiled almost tenderly where once the curve of his mouth had shown evidence of sardonic amusement or contempt.

With their visitors he was both patient and courteous, the obvious proof of good breeding.

Invariably they were very late for breakfast, a circumstance that more than satisfied their hosts, since they preferred to breakfast outside on the patio, while Harold preferred to eat in the house.

"I expect we shall have to take them somewhere today." The disconsolate edge to Helen's voice brought the trace of a smile to her husband's lips, and he shook his head in a gesture of faint reproof.

"Do try to be a little more gracious about it," he advised. "It'll be far more comfortable for you yourself in addition to making things more pleasant for our visitors." He paused, but she maintained a frowning silence. "It would be the height of bad manners, Helen, for you to let them see how you feel."

"I know," she agreed flatly, "but it's exceedingly difficult even to be patient sometimes, especially with Harold."

He nodded and said,

"He has been trying, I admit. He's the most objectionable man I've ever had the misfortune to meet, and the more I see of him the less can I understand how your mother came to marry him."

"Perhaps she was lonely."

"Weren't you at home?"

"Yes, but there's never been any sort of closeness between Mother and me."

Again he nodded, his gaze thoughtful.

"It's strange that it should be so. Between my mother and me there has always been a close relationship."

At this Helen smiled; Nick saw the reason and responded instantly. Helen said, voicing what was in both their minds,

"She understands you too."

A shrug and then,

131

"I don't believe in deceit. In any case, Mother's no fool; unlike your stepfather she's realistic about life – and morals." Helen merely coloured slightly and with the reappearance of his smile her husband said, "It wouldn't have pleased her at all had I lived the life of a celibate. In Greece it is considered that an inexperienced man is a namby-pamby." Another pause as he gazed at her with an amused expression. "It's also an accepted fact that women have a preference for the experienced man." A question was hinted at and she offered an answer without thinking beforehand.

"Never having had any – er – dealings with an inexperienced man I wouldn't know."

His eyes glinted; he said softly,

"I hope you haven't, Helen."

Her eyes flashed.

"A man with a past like yours has no right to expect to marry a girl who hasn't been around."

His dark eyes widened and his brows lifted.

"In Greece we don't merely expect – we demand."

"But you can't know," she challenged, feeling that the subject should be dropped yet impelled somehow to carry it on.

"Mostly we know, because as I've said, marriages are arranged, and this means that a thorough investigation is made into the girl's history. Should there be a black mark against her character then she has little chance of finding a husband."

"It all sounds very outdated to me," she said.

"Because in your country you have no morals any more. I really don't know why anyone gets married at all."

132

"People still fall in love." She spoke softly now because she was acutely aware of her own love, and of the desire to impress the word on her husband's mind. But she felt depressed suddenly, having to face the fact that love to a Greek was a word to be sneered at – at least, when its reference affected the relationship between a man and a woman. Greeks loved their parents and their children; they loved their aged relatives, never failing to care for them personally. During the time she had lived and worked in Greece Helen had learned a great deal about the Greek character and way of life, and she had never once heard of an aged person being put into an institution.

"And fall out of love just as speedily," came Nick's cynical rejoinder. "They then have all the trouble of divorce. Here, we might not fall in love, but our marriages do last."

"Many people must be unhappy, though," she pointed out. And she added, "I know for a fact that they are because I've heard of several cases where the wife is left alone while the husband goes off to spend his evenings with some other woman."

He frowned at this and she saw with some surprise that he did not approve.

"I must admit that you're right," he owned at length. "But it is a situation which I deplore. In my opinion a man should never marry unless he is absolutely sure that the woman of his choice will satisfy him completely." He stopped and humour suddenly lit his eyes. "I embarrass you, my Helen, but you should be flattered – very flattered. Before I met you marriage was the last thing in my mind, for no woman had held so strong a position as

133

you. In other words, I had not met a woman of whom I would not eventually tire."

She said, swallowing a hurtful little lump in her throat, "It wasn't really marriage you wanted, though – not at first."

The reminder brought another frown to his brow.

"I believe that I would have married you, though, even had you consented to –" He stopped and the frown became heavy and his expression angry. "I think we'll allow this matter to drop," he said shortly. "There are certain episodes in one's life that are best forgotten."

Such surprising words, and this angry look that marred his features. . . .

Her eyes searched his, and because emotion filled her her mouth trembled slightly. Colour added enchantment to her cheeks and the sun in her hair transformed it to pure gold. Behind her a riot of colour formed an exotic backcloth to a breathtakingly lovely picture, and Nick caught his breath. That he fully appreciated her beauty she had never been in doubt, since not only did his eyes reveal it but he never tired of remarking on it. But what good was this sort of attraction when its effect was to arouse desire only? Yet he had said, just once, that he was beginning to think that it was more than her beauty that attracted him.

If only she could think that it was love. . . .

It was too soon yet to cherish such an attractive and acceptable idea, but she resolved that from now on there would never be a moment's disunion between them; she would strive to awaken him to the fact that a spiritual relationship could exist alongside the physical one that up till now appeared to be all that interested him.

Nick drove them all to Mytilene, the capital of the island and which, like that of most Greek islands, had the same name as the island itself. The drive was delightful, taking them through countryside where trees abounded, through olive groves and roads bordered by tall grasses and oleanders and flowering Judas trees. Peasant women were seen on the sunlit hillsides, tending their sheep and goats; the lovely outline of the Turkish coast rose up from a sea of dazzling aquamarine banded with channels of jade running sinuously beneath the surface of the water.

Harold said grudgingly,

"This is a very attractive island. You're a fortunate young woman, Helen." He turned his head, for Helen had obligingly sat in the back of the car with her mother, so that Harold could sit in the front with Nick. His crimped hair filled her with disgust; she scarcely had the patience to speak to him. However, she did manage to reply, and miraculously injected a ring of pleasantry into her voice.

"I realize that I'm fortunate. The island's a dream and I love it."

"We had no idea that it would be like this," from her mother, who was looking out at the tree-clothed chain of low hills through which they were at present passing. "Harold thought it would be bleak and barren, as are so many of the Greek islands."

"Lesbos has always been thickly wooded," Nick informed her. "For this reason it is in fact one of the most beautiful of our islands."

"We must come again," from Mrs Lynch with a sigh. "Now that we have Helen living in so lovely a place we

135

ought to take advantage of it and come every year."

A silence fell; Helen had the impression that her husband was smiling amusedly to himself, knowing as he did just how she herself would be receiving this decision of her mother's. The silence endured for a long while until at last Nick broke it by saying that they were almost at the capital.

"We shall soon see the harbour and the castle." He took a bend in the road and the town came into view. After parking the car he took them to an expensive hotel for lunch and then they strolled round the town, the main street of which was in effect a long bazaar. Mrs. Lynch suggested they split up, as she and Harold wanted to explore the shops for souvenirs and presents to take home to their friends.

"Fine," said Helen with perhaps a little too much enthusiasm. "We'll meet later, then?"

"My dear Helen," Nick was saying a few minutes later, "your manners are beginning to leave a lot to be desired."

"Was I too eager to let them go?"

"You positively gave them a push!"

She bit her lip.

"Will they have noticed, do you think?"

He glanced down at her as she walked by his side towards the Turkish castle standing on the peninsula.

"Had it been me I certainly should have noticed. However, I don't expect Harold noticed." A small pause ensued. "Your enthusiasm wasn't so potently displayed when your mother suggested they come to us every year," he remarked in some amusement, and Helen shook her head at once.

136

"I couldn't bear it. Mother I could perhaps endure, but not Harold. We never have got on, as you can imagine."

"It must have been a blow to you when he took up residence in your home?"

"I didn't stay long. There wasn't room for both of us."

"I can understand that."

"It will be awful if they do decide to come over every year."

"We shall have to think up some excuse for not having them," he said.

"Do you suppose they've really enjoyed themselves?" she asked, and her husband immediately responded with,

"Do I detect a hint of anxiety not untinged with guilt in your voice?"

She gave a slight start.

"Is it so obvious?"

His dark eyes held an amused expression as he said,

"Your contrition is obvious, yes. But don't worry, child, they haven't noticed anything."

"Are you sure?" she asked anxiously.

"Quite. There's no coolness that I have noticed – at least, not since that first day when, soon after their arrival, you had a few words with them about something which you chose to keep secret from me."

She frowned and said,

"Don't ask me about it, Nick. I want to forget about it."

To her relief he merely shrugged and changed the subject, beginning to tell her about the history of the town and of the island itself. They had reached the castle and had found a seat under a tree. He talked, in that low attractive voice which she had come to love, telling her of the pre-history people – the Pelasgians and others who lived on the island twelve hundred years before the birth of Christ.

"So long ago? I wonder what they were like?"

"We shall never know," he said with an indifferent shrug. "We do have written history of those that came later, though, among whom were Pittacus, one of the Seven Sages, and the poets, Alcaeus and Sappho."

"Sappho. . . . Everyone's heard of her. She was the head of a literary society, wasn't she?"

"A female literary society," he amended without much expression. Helen said no more, but she was thinking about those ancient times when the high-bred ladies used to occupy their time writing poetry – sometimes the most passionate poetry – about each other. And so Lesbos acquired an infamous reputation, and that was why the name had been changed to Mytilene.

After a while Nick and Helen got up and after strolling about the precincts of the castle made for the waterfront where they found a quiet tree-shaded café and sat outside in the sunshine drinking iced cordial. Inside, men danced to *bouzouki* music, leaping and twisting and frequently coming to the wide, open doorway so as to provide entertainment for Nick and Helen and also the one or two tourists who were sitting there.

At last they went off to meet Helen's mother and her husband at the appointed place. Politely Nick said,

"I see you've managed to find something to suit you." Holding out a hand, he took two parcels from Mrs. Lynch and carried them back to the car. Harold grumbled about the high prices, causing Helen to feel more

138

ashamed of him than ever. She cast an apologetic glance at Nick, who shook his head faintly, silently telling her not to get herself worked up about so trivial a matter. He then made the comment that as there were no tourists on the island during the winter the shopkeepers had to make their money during the summer.

"That's all very well," muttered Harold, "but it's no excuse for their exploiting us."

A contemptuous glance flicked him and he coloured as he sent Nick in return an insolent look.

"The choice is yours," was Nick's gentle reminder. "The shopkeepers don't ask you to buy."

"But they pester you," put in Mrs. Lynch on seeing her husband's discomfiture. "One woman brought out about two dozen hand-woven rugs, one after another. We just couldn't get away."

"Did you buy one?" asked Helen, feeling she must make some contribution towards easing the situation before one or other of them lost his temper.

"We had to," snapped Harold.

"I'm sure," returned Nick with admirable restraint, "you'll enjoy owning one of those delightful rugs. You'll be the envy of your friends."

"I doubt it. They look cheap to me."

They were back at the car and Helen gave a deep sigh of relief. Four more days ... they would seem like an eternity.

It was much later when, not having been very clever, she found herself alone with her stepfather. She had changed for dinner and come down on to the verandah to enjoy a few minutes on her own before Nick appeared and drinks were served. She had felt exhausted after the day out with her mother and Harold and had decided she needed to find a quiet place in which to recover. But no sooner had she settled herself comfortably in a low luxuriously-upholstered armchair than Harold appeared, smelling of cheap scent or talc or after-shave lotion – she could not decide which. All she knew was that she was glad of the breeze which wafted it away fairly quickly.

"Ah," he said, taking possession of a chair, "it's cool out here! I'm not at all happy in the sort of heat you get in Greece. It isn't healthy, for one thing. I keep telling your mother this and at last she agrees with me. You have mosquitoes, I've noticed, and those dreadful things that whirr incessantly in the trees."

"The cicadas? We get used to them and for the most part we don't hear them."

"Nonsense! You can't help hearing them. And those dreadful lizards too, that dart up the walls." Breaking off, he shuddered, and Helen's lip curled in contempt. "I don't know how you can live with all these creatures annoying you."

"The geckos are harmless, and as it happens they're useful because they eat insects."

"Well, I prefer not to have the insects at all. Since coming here I've really begun to appreciate my own country." He paused, but Helen's patience was running out and she decided not to take any risks with it. And so she remained silent, faintly smiling to herself as one of the offending lizards came from a warm stone and poised itself on the edge of the verandah, its long slender tongue flicking in and out with incredible swiftness. "I suppose, though," resumed Harold, unable, as usual, to sit quietly and enjoy the garden and the view beyond, "that there are compensations in your life. It isn't every day that a girl of your station manages to get herself married to a wealthy ship-owner." His glance strayed to the diamond and ruby bracelet she wore. "Your husband's a generous man, obviously." He was now looking at her dress, a delightful creation in white crystal satin, and of Edwardian style. "You'd be a fool to jeopardize your position, wouldn't you?"

She flashed him a glance, her nerves on the alert.

"What do you mean?"

He shrugged and it seemed as if he would refrain from offering a reply. But his meddlesome nature prevailed and he spoke of Paul, saying again that he had no right to be writing to her secretly and reasserting his conviction that she and Paul had been having an affair.

"You'd better watch your step," he warned finally. "From what I've seen of Nick during our stay here I'd say he wasn't the type to stand any nonsense."

White with fury, Helen looked straight at him and asked,

"Just what do you mean by nonsense?"

"He'll not stand for anything underhand. And something underhand is going on," he added quickly as she would have interrupted him. "Dare you show Nick the letter we brought you from Paul?"

"Its contents can have no interest for him whatsoever," she replied frigidly. "And now, do you mind if we drop the subject?"

"Evasion again!" His voice was a sneer and she felt that if he kept on she would have to get up and leave him. "This evasion is in effect an admittance that you dare not show Paul's letter to your. . . ." His voice trailed away and, turning, Helen felt her heart jerk right into her throat. For, standing just behind her, was Nick, his black eyes glinting strangely, his hands clenched tightly at his sides.

"Who," Nick was saying with dangerous quiet much later when their visitors had gone to bed, "is Paul?"

"Paul?" She swallowed hard, her fear and dejection mingling as they had been doing all the evening. For she had known without any doubt at all that Nick had heard at least part of her conversation with Harold. It could be that he had heard most of it, as the room from which he had come was heavily curtained, Julia having practically closed the curtains in order to keep out the fierce heat of the sun. And so Nick could very well have been standing there for some time, and as the only words that rang incessantly in her brain were those spoken when Harold had said there was something underhand going on, and his immediate question, "Dare you show Nick the letter we brought you from Paul?" she had been in a state of nervous tension right through dinner and the interminable hours that had followed. Nick's face had been taut the whole time; his conversation had been polite as usual but very limited. His mind was occupied by something else; this was evidenced by his brooding, thoughtful expression. It was not difficult for Helen to guess just what it was that caused this preoccupation.

And Harold. . . . How she hated him! He too had been aware that he had been overheard – and he was clearly gloating over it. She felt convinced that it was his vindictive hope that she would be in trouble with her husband.

And she was. No doubt about it. But what must she say to him? She had lied several times already, but not so cleverly that suspicion had not been planted in his mind. And with suspicion there already what hope had she of extricating herself unharmed?

"Yes, Paul." So soft the tone, but the danger was still there. Again she swallowed, her misery welling up as it was borne in on her that only a short while ago she had cherished the hope that, partly by her own endeavours, she might eventually find herself admired for something far different from her beauty. But what price her hopes now?

"He's – he's the husband of a friend of mine."

The black eyes flickered and she caught her breath. Had he made a guess already? He was so astute, so quick to grasp a situation.

"The husband of a friend? Have you ever mentioned these friends to me?"

"I don't think so." She felt convinced that guilt was written all over her face and for one despairing second she decided that it were best to make a full confession and get it over and done with. But what deterred her, when she gave the matter more thought, was the fact that she had lied and, later, had evaded his questions, leaving him suspicious, while she herself had dreaded his ever discovering the truth.

"From what I overheard this evening it would appear that this Paul has written to you? May I see his letter?"

The question she had known must come. She said huskily,

"It isn't possible, Nick. The contents are personal."

He looked at her piercingly, his nostrils quivering, his

mouth tight. Once again she was reminded of her sure conviction that in jealousy he would be a fiend.

"I might as well tell you, Helen," he said at last, "that I overheard enough to be sure that the contents of that letter would interest me exceedingly." She looked appealingly at him but could not speak. "Are you going to show it to me?" he inquired softly after a while.

"I can't," she cried desperately. "Please don't ask me to! And – and let the matter drop, for truly it isn't important – not now...." Would he grasp what those two simple words were meant to convey? But no; he was too inflamed by what he had overheard, and by her refusal to show him the letter. She could understand just how he felt and yet she tried again to avoid a scene. "I swear to you that it's not important. Please believe me, Nick, I beg of you." Her voice was low, and beseeching in its tone. But his mouth remained inflexible; his whole bearing was cold and magisterial. He stood like a judge, and suddenly she could not be meek and humble any more; he was unwilling to listen to her plea – and more than willing to create a scene, so he could have one! "I'm not showing you my letter, and that's final!"

The swift change seemed to take him by surprise, for he gave a slight start. But he recovered instantly and took a wrathful step towards her. "And if you make one small move to hurt me physically," she threatened, "I shall call out, and not only will Mother and Harold hear me, but the servants as well!"

He stopped, and she saw the muscle working in the side of his jaw. No doubt about it, he was in a towering rage.

"I see," through his teeth. "Well, my girl, you might have won this round, but the game isn't played out yet!"

144

Something in his tone caused her heart to flutter; she asked him what he meant. She would see, he replied, his eyes glinting with fury.

"I don't see what you can do to me," she said defiantly. "Moreover, I'm amazed that you should question my rights to privacy at all. I never demand to see the letters you receive."

"They're business letters."

"So you say. But what proof have I?" Unhappiness caused her to say these things, things which she would rather have left unsaid, since they had no real meaning or importance. She was convinced that he spoke the truth when he declared that his letters were all business ones.

He looked at her hard and long, his mouth moving strangely, his expression now one of . . . could it possibly be pain? But no; she dismissed so ridiculous an idea. He could be hurt only if he loved her. . . . Her thoughts wandered, picking up incidents that had impressed her; she was also reminded of that lost moment when she had been so close to asking him if he loved her. She opened her mouth to speak, to ask him outright if he was hurt by her refusal to show him the letter. And in the same instant she was deciding that if he should say yes then she would confess all – and ask that they begin again. By this request she would in effect be telling him of her love. But he spoke before her, in that hard unyielding voice, telling her that, if it would be of any interest to her, she could read every letter that came to him.

"I've never given you cause to doubt me," he added in a harsh-edged tone, "so your comments are plainly aimed at excusing your own conduct."

This was true, in part, and she averted her head; it

was a gesture of guilt, an admission that her husband was correct in his assumption.

She said at length in a quivering tone,

"Nick . . . can't we forget all about the letter –?"

"Forget? You've received a communication from a man, a letter brought by your mother so that there was no risk of my seeing it, and you calmly ask me to forget it? What sort of a fool do you take me for? If there's nothing of an intimate nature in that letter then why can't you let me see it?"

"Because it's my own private property," she snapped, distress bringing out her temper again. "I won't show it to you, so you might as well resign yourself to this!"

The black eyes narrowed to mere slits. Helen instinctively stepped back even though she guessed the action might inflame him.

"I can't force you to show it to me," he rasped, "but, as I've just said, the game's not played out yet!"

CHAPTER NINE

IT never occurred to Helen that, having realized that he had been the cause of creating trouble between Nick and herself, Harold would decide to afford himself further malicious pleasure by openly making comments that would add fuel to the fire.

The first time he did this was at lunch the following day when, having seen the coldness with which Nick and Helen treated one another, he asked with well-feigned anxiety,

"Is something wrong between you two? I'm feeling dreadfully guilty, because I'm convinced that you overheard something I was saying to Helen last evening."

She glared at him, while Nick's dark contemptuous eyes raked him from head to foot. It was clear that whatever his feelings towards her, he found no excuse for Harold's malicious words.

"I think we'll talk about something else," was Nick's frigid reply, and Harold shrugged his narrow shoulders in a gesture of resignation. But his wife was puzzled and wanted to know more about it.

"I seem to have been left in the dark," she complained. "Why should you ask if something's wrong between Helen and Nick?"

"They're not over-friendly, you must have noticed it."

Helen gasped at this outspokenness, while Nick, his mouth tight, ignored the remark and gave his whole attention to his food.

"Have you quarrelled?" asked Mrs. Lynch imperturbably. "I expect you'll make it up in no time at all."

The second time Harold tried to increase the ill-feeling between husband and wife was on the day they were leaving. Nick had driven them to the airport and as they had over an hour to wait Nick invited them to have a drink. Harold was suddenly all simpering apology as he said,

"I do hope no permanent damage was done that evening. Helen assured me, Nick, that the contents of the letter which we brought over from her friend would not interest you in the least. Er ... perhaps you should believe this and forget the matter altogether." A twisted smile which seemed to send the receding chin back still further and then, "We're living in times when young

147

people tend to disregard the codes which we older ones regard as important, and, if Helen *has* committed an indiscretion, then you should try your best to overlook it." He turned to Helen. "I've done my best for you," he said with a return of his sickly smile. "And I hope my words to your husband have gone home, and that this quarrel will soon be made up. Your happiness is – and always has been since the day I became your stepfather – one of deep concern to me."

Fire looked out from her eyes, reflecting the burning fury within; but there was a short time only to go, and with a restraint of which she would never have believed herself capable, Helen managed to hold back the bitter words of criticism and denunciation which hovered on her lips. But she made the solemn vow that never again would she have Harold here to stay. In fact, as she felt at this moment, she sincerely hoped she would never set eyes on him again.

"That's the kindest thing for you to say, Harold," put in his wife. "I'm sure dear Helen is grateful for your interest in her welfare." Turning to her daughter as she spoke, she inserted a question into her tone.

"I think it is time you drank up," intervened Nick, showing consideration for his wife in spite of the hostility he felt towards her. "You haven't much time left."

A short while later he and Helen were driving home in silence, a silence which she desperately wished to break but could not. A great heaviness had settled on her, a heaviness that was fast increasing to deep desolation now that she and Nick were once again on their own. If only she had not agreed to have her mother and Harold over on the visit! But it was too late for regrets; the damage was done, and as she felt at this moment the future looked so bleak that it seemed to hold nothing but continued disunion between her husband and herself. He would never unbend from this frigid attitude he had adopted towards her; he would always harbour distrust because she had refused to show him Paul's letter.

To her amazement he said, as soon as they arrived back at the villa,

"I'm going out. Don't wait up for me; I'll not be home before midnight."

"Midnight?" she repeated, the colour leaving her face. "Where are you going?" Why she should suspect him of going out with another woman she did not know. It was absurd in the extreme, she tried to tell herself, remembering that Nick had deplored the fact of a man going out with someone other than his wife.

"That," he said icily, "is my business." He strode away and she stared after his retreating figure, her lip quivering, her eyes misted by tears.

It was past one o'clock when he came in. Lying awake, Helen heard him in his room, moving about. And then silence. Swinging over on to her side, she buried her face in the pillow and let fall the tears that had hung so heavily behind her eyes for the whole of the time he had been away.

The following evening it was the same, and the one after that. Once he said,

"Are you going to show me that letter, Helen?" And when she had said no he left her and went out to the garage. Helen watched the car roll along the gravel path to the road, watched it disappear round a bend, a cloud of dust rising up in its wake, as if the driver had put his foot right down suddenly.

When a week had passed, and the rift had widened into a great gulf, Helen began seriously to wonder whether she could continue like this for the rest of her life. For in her present unhappy state of mind the situation between Nick and herself took on an almost sinister aspect and she found no difficulty at all in visualising a future of loneliness and uncertainty, this latter stemming from Nick's refusal to say where he was spending his time. That he had taken this particular line more than a little surprised her, as threats and a show of temper would have been more characteristic of his personality as she had come to know it.

Running alongside her unhappiness was the anxiety as to whether or not Paul would carry out his threat and come over to Greece. She had not replied to his letter, nor had she any intention of doing so, but she knew instinctively that this would in no way crush his hopes. The fact that he had remained undaunted by her marriage proved this. It was clear that he intended putting up a fight to win her, believing, with his stubborn confidence, that in the end she would be prevailed upon to leave her husband. His whole attitude was irrational – but how was she to bring this home to him?

As the days passed an urgency entered into her; she knew for sure that Paul would come. The only solution that presented itself to her was that she should go to England, and make it clear to Paul that there was no hope at all for him, as she was now in love with her husband. But how to get to England was the problem, for without doubt Nick would raise objections to her going alone. At length her anxiety reached a point where she could bear it no longer, for every day she woke wondering if this would be the day on which Paul would appear. And so she tentatively mentioned to Nick that she would like to visit her friend Lily, in Birmingham. His eyes narrowed, but so fleetingly that she was not sure, afterwards, if she had imagined this slight indication of suspicion on her husband's part. To her amazement he said indifferently,

"Go if you want to." And then, "How long will you be away?"

Helen looked at him through misted eyes. So sure she had been that he would raise objections, but instead he seemed almost eager for her to go on the visit. She was inordinately relieved, of course, at this unexpected agreement with her plan, but, paradoxically, his failure to object hurt intolerably, since it proved beyond any doubt at all that her attraction for him was losing its strength. He did not care if she went away; he would not miss her. His whole manner gave evidence of this and, once she was alone in her room, Helen gave way to bitter tears.

There was no hope for the marriage, she convinced herself miserably. Already Nick had found someone else; he must have done so, for otherwise he would not be going off every evening and returning very late at night.

It was Nick himself who arranged for her flight; this conduct did nothing for her spirits, but determinedly she kept her unhappiness hidden and she was able to appear cheerful and eager when eventually she was being driven to the airport.

"Enjoy yourself," he said laconically as he left her . . . and as he did not turn as he walked away he failed to see the swift movement of his wife's hand as she flicked a tear from her cheek.

Arriving in England at three in the afternoon, she caught a train to her destination, the town nearest to where Paul and Fran lived. There were only three hotels and she managed to get a room at the smallest. It was too late to phone Paul at the office and so immediately after dinner she went to bed. When she rang the following morning one of the office staff informed her that Paul was out on business for the firm but would be back later in the day.

"I should imagine it will be about half-past three," the girl said. "Can I ask him to ring you?"

"No, it's quite all right. I'll ring him."

This she did; Paul seemed dazed on hearing her voice, but soon recovered, speaking in a tone which rang with triumph.

"I should have known you'd come to me! How did you manage it? – the getting away from your husband, I mean? Didn't he offer any objection to your coming to England? What did you tell him?"

An angry intake of Helen's breath was his only answer as for a long moment she maintained a silence.

"I told him I was coming to visit Lily," she said at last. "However, my real reason is –"

"That you can see me," he broke in triumphantly. "It only goes to show how strong the pull is! But if you hadn't come, Helen, I was coming to you within the week. I've already told Fran that I'm having to go away no business, so the way for my visit to you was paved. I would have phoned you from Athens –"

"Paul," she interrupted with wrathful urgency, it being imperative that she bring to an end what he was saying, "just listen to me instead of talking all that nonsense! I'm here to talk to you seriously, to convince you once

152

and for all that there can never be anything between you and me. Can you get away from work?"

He made no reply for several moments.

"I don't think I understand. I've seen Harold — met him by accident the other day — and he told me you weren't happy with your husband. He said trouble had been caused because your husband got to know about my letter."

Helen's fingers clenched about the receiver; her face was white with fury.

"Harold had no right to talk about Nick and me! And for your information he's got it all wrong!"

"I don't think so," with returning confidence. "You wouldn't be here if everything *were* all right between you an Nick –"

"I've told you, I've come only in order to convince you that I want to be left alone. I'm not having you inter-fering in my life, and it's this that's brought me. You had no right to visit my mother, and most certainly you ought not to have asked her to deliver a letter to me." She paused but he made no comment. "Can you meet me, now?" she then asked.

"I can't just walk out of the office," he snapped in tones that betrayed without any doubt at all his rising anger. "I'll see you at five o'clock."

"That will do very well." Helen paused a moment in thought. "We'll have tea together – at the Salt Cellar –"

"That place? In a back alley? No, we'll go to the Grosvenor."

"I'm not going anywhere where we're likely to be seen!"

"Does it matter? Everyone'll know soon enough."

"The Salt Cellar — at five," she returned, then replaced the receiver without affording him the opportunity of making any further protest.

Paul arrived on time, meeting her outside the café. His eyes wore a brooding expression, but his admiration for her was clearly displayed for all that. He seemed for a long moment to be taking in everything about her, while saying how good it was to be seeing her. He took her arm as they entered the small dimly-lit room where one or two other people were taking afternoon tea.

"I can't go on," he said presently. "I'm crazy about you — and I know you care for me. . . ." His voice fell to silence as the waitress approached their table, the table Helen had chosen because it was tucked away in a corner, out of the line of light streaming in through the glass door. Away from this shaft the dimness prevailed.

"Just tea and a sandwich," said Helen politely after the merest glance at the menu. Paul ordered the same, waiting only until the girl had turned her back before leaning across the table. But before he could speak Helen was saying,

"I meant what I said on the phone, Paul. I've come over for one reason only, that of convincing you that there can never be anything between you and me. I happen to love my husband, and so you'll now accept the fact that there's not the slightest possibility of my ever leaving him." She stopped, furious because Paul was shaking his head, silently telling her he did not believe what she was saying. "*I love Nick!*" she repeated with emphasis. A scornful glance was cast across the table. "Why won't you be a man and face up to the truth?"

He went red as anger and embarrassment rose together.

"I can't believe you've fallen in love with him," was his stubborn comment after a long pause. "You'll not deny that you married him because you feared you'd betray Fran?"

Helen glanced away.

"I wouldn't say that," she prevaricated. "I must have *wanted* to marry him, mustn't I?" She was recalling her idea at that time, the idea that Nick had by his powerful personality exerted some influence on her. Looking back now she knew that even at that time, when she felt she detested him, stamping him as immoral, she must have been drawn to him in some way, for otherwise how could she have come so quickly to love him? And never once since her marriage had she known an aversion to him. Self-shame, yes, but not once had she been in any way disgusted with Nick himself.

"You married him in order to safeguard Fran," Paul was declaring. "Don't deny it, Helen, because you can't deceive either yourself or me. We both know how we feel —"

"How am I to convince you?" broke in Helen wrathfully. "I've said that I love my husband, and I mean it!"

Paul's face darkened; he became thoughtful and she saw at last to her satisfaction that he was beginning to accept what she had been so desperately trying to put over to him.

Nevertheless, he once again brought up the reason for her marrying Nick, and this time she did go as far as to own that Paul was correct in his declaration that she would never have considered marriage to him had it not been for the dire necessity of putting a barrier between herself and Paul.

"You say you must have wanted to marry him," Paul said musingly. "But you've now admitted that this wasn't true?"

"I can't explain," she told him impatiently. "Moreover, I don't intend to try. I suppose what really influenced me at that time was your saying that had I also been married then the difficulties would have been greater. I was terribly afraid that you were on the verge of confessing all to Fran, and so I agreed to marry Nick." On noting the lift of Paul's brows she answered the unspoken question by saying that Nick had previously proposed to her, having taken her out several times when she was in Greece.

"Was he in love with you?" asked Paul bluntly, his gaze fixing hers.

"What has that to do with it?" she almost snapped.

"You've admitted by this evasion that he wasn't in love with you. I've heard of these Greeks and their atitude towards marriage. They think only of one thing –"

"Please, Paul," she interrupted, "accept the situation and leave it at that. I came here, as I've said, in order to ensure that you'll not decide to come over to see me in Greece. It would only upset my life even more than it's upset at present –" She broke off, aghast at what she had revealed. Paul's eyes narrowed suddenly.

"So you're not happy?" he observed, a bitter note entering his voice. "Was it my letter that caused the upset you mention?"

"My husband didn't care for the idea of another man

writing to me – which is understandable."

"Were you happy before he came to learn of the letter?"

"Yes, we were –"

"Don't lie! You're no good at it! It's easy to see that although you're in love with your husband you're also afraid of him. It's also plain that he doesn't love you."

Helen made no comment on this, since she had practically admitted that Nick didn't love her.

"How's Fran?" she asked, abruptly changing the subject.

"So-so," with an indifferent shrug. "She's getting used to the idea that the marriage won't last."

Helen's eyes glinted.

"You're so callous about it. I don't know how you could have fallen out of love with Fran so easily."

He looked at her.

"I met you," he returned broodingly.

"If you hadn't, you'd now be happy in your marriage." Helen spoke with deep regret, cursing fate – and her own attraction for this man, an attraction that, no matter what the future might hold for him and Fran, had ruined the first months of his marriage, a period so precious that its loss was tragic. "Why don't you make up your mind to forget me?" she asked, shaking her head in censure. "Fran's sweet, Paul, and she loves you dearly. You're a lucky man, for girls like her are scarce."

He was frowning impatiently even as she spoke. Fran might be something special, he owned, but what did that profit him if he wasn't in love with her?

"I can't bear her near me," he ended, and Helen's eyes widened as she stared at him, appalled. Guilt was already

157

weighing heavily upon her, but this stark admission made her feel just about as low as any woman could feel. Consciously she had done nothing to bring about her friend's unhappiness, but unconsciously she, and only she, had brought Fran untold misery. "I think all the time about you," Paul was saying, then his voice faded as the waitress came up with the tray.

"I'm not hungry." Helen frowned as the plate was put before her. "All I want from you, Paul," she continued looking straight at him, "is your promise that you'll neither communicate with me nor try to see me. My home's now in Greece, my place with my husband, just as your place is with Fran – Oh, yes, it is, no matter what you say! You married her, after making her fall in love with you, and it's incumbent on you to try to make her happy. Forget me – this is the only way, because it's profitless to go on the way you've been doing. I never loved you –"

"You did!" he cut in violently. "For both of us it was love at first sight."

Helen sighed angrily but made no comment on this assertion. All she wanted was to get away from Paul, having no desire even to take the meal with him. As if to emphasise her intention she picked up her handbag from the chair beside her and made to rise from the table.

"Your promise, Paul; that's all I want from you before we say good-bye for the last time. I don't ever want to see you again as long as I live."

"You're going?" All the spirit went out of him suddenly, and his eyes were glazed by misery. "I can't live without you, Helen," he quivered. "I love you. And as it's obvious that you're not happy with your husband. . . ." His voice trailed away to silence as she drew an impatient breath. "Don't go yet," he begged in tones of pleading. "Give me this one memory – this one hour."

"Paul," she said quietly, managing only with difficulty to hide her compassion, "forget me. Other people have been in a similar position and have got over it. You'd soon do the same if you made up your mind to put me out of your thoughts once and for all."

"It's obvious that you don't any longer care," he admitted after a long pause. "I've let my opportunity slip by. I was too slow at first." He spoke pensively, almost to himself. Helen again made no comment, for argument was futile. She said quietly,

"Your promise is what I'm waiting for, Paul. Give it to me and let me go."

"Very well." A great shuddering sigh accompanied the promise. "But if ever you find that your life too becomes unbearable –"

"It won't, Paul."

"Your husband doesn't love you," he said, looking into her eyes. "Your marriage might not last."

"It will last. However, even if it didn't, I should never come to you, for the simple reason that I don't care for you in that way."

He looked down, mumbling to himself, saying once again that he had allowed his opportunity to slip by. For a second or two Helen dwelt on that scene when in his lunch hour he had come to her home. Had she not run from him, had he exerted a forcefulness – such as Nick would have exerted, she thought – then what would have been the outcome? Would she have succumbed to whatever it was she at that time felt for Paul? Perhaps . . . but only

159

if Paul had shown the strength and determination of her husband. . . . No, not otherwise. She gave a thankful and satisfied sigh as she admitted this. To have given way to a man like Paul would have been shameful; to give way to a man with Nick's forceful mastery and dominance could quite reasonably be excused.

"When are you going back?" inquired Paul at last.

"Quite soon," she replied gently.

"Please have your tea with me."

She hesitated. Having received his promise she desired only to get away. However, she agreed to stay and have her tea. But it was eaten in near silence, with both of them feeling tense and awkward. It was a relief when at last they left the café and went out into the street.

"You're staying with Lily tonight?"

She shook her head.

"I'm staying at an hotel."

"You told your husband you were visiting Lily. You might as well go and see her." He was speaking for the sake of holding her, and Helen had once again to hide her compassion, for undoubtedly he was suffering.

"Lily would only ask awkward questions which I'm not in the mood to answer. I'll have a couple of days in London and then go home."

"Won't your husband think the visit's been short?"

She nodded mechanically.

"Perhaps I'll stay a little longer in London. There's always plenty to do there."

He paused and then, in a dull yet pleading tone,

"Won't you let me come with you — just for these few days? We'll go to the museums and to a show in the evenings."

Helen shook her head emphatically.

"It would do no good to either of us," she pointed out, then added in a gentle voice, "This is good-bye, Paul." He seemed to be prevented from speaking by something in his throat, for he swallowed over and over again. Helen waited a while, then ventured to ask, "Will you now try your very best to settle down with Fran? Promise me, Paul, that at least you'll make some effort."

Dumbly he stood there, looking into her troubled face, his mouth moving spasmodically. Becoming more and more uncomfortable with the passing of each silent moment, Helen made an uneasy movement, indicating that she was ready to go. Paul managed to speak at last, his voice husky and quivering,

"I don't know what I shall do. I feel I just can't settle down with Fran – and yet –" He spread his hands hopelessly. "What else is there for me now?"

Helen's eyes filled up.

"Try to love her as you used to," she pleaded and, turning, she walked swiftly away, taking the first corner to which she came, so as to be quickly lost to his view.

Utterly exhausted and drained by the meeting with Paul, and with her struggle to make him accept the situation, Helen went back to her hotel and, going up to her room, she lay stretched out on the bed, trying to relax and to rid herself of the tension that had built up within her. She had the promise for which she had come, but although this was a great relief she was acutely conscious of the fact that her troubles were by no means at an end.

However, she was too tired to begin dwelling on her future and what her relationship with her husband was likely to be. Surely with time all problems would resolve themselves, she thought, her mind gradually becoming hazy as sleep crept in upon her.

It was almost eight o'clock when, awakened by the telephone, she turned on her side and picked up the receiver. There was a gentleman to see her, she was told – a gentleman who said the matter was urgent. The name was given and she frowned heavily. Paul. . . . What on earth did he want now?

"I'll be down directly," she said, but before she could replace the receiver the night porter was saying,

"The gentleman says it is better that you talk in private. He wants to come up to your room."

Her frown deepened, but after a moment she agreed that Paul should come up.

"What do you want?" she demanded furiously almost before he had entered the room. "And how did you discover where I'm staying?"

"That was easy. There are only three hotels in the town. I got you on the second phone call." The merest pause and then, in the sort of dramatic voice Harold would have used, "Your husband's in England –"

"My husband?" Helen's face drained of colour. "But how –? I mean, where have you got this information?" Dazed by the news, she grasped at once that Nick had followed her to England. This meant that he suspected her of deceit . . . suspected her of coming to see Paul, not Lily. How stupid she had been! Looking back now she saw with startling clarity that she had fallen into a trap – a trap of her own setting but of which her husband had instantly taken advantage. Yes, his ready agreement for her to come to England was quite clearly explained now.

"Apparently he hadn't believed your tale about a visit

to Lily," began Paul, when an impatient wave of her hand cut him short.

"I've already deduced that much. How do you know he's here –?" Her heart caught and then gave a great lurch. "He's seen you . . . talked to you?"

Paul shook his head.

"He went to Lily's, naturally. She hadn't a notion that you were in England, and because she was taken by surprise she told your husband this. He then asked for my address and she had given it to him before she had time to think what it all might be about. As soon as he had gone she rang me, but I was out and so was Fran – which was lucky, in a way. Lily rang again about an hour ago after having tried every half hour or so. She was mightily curious, I can tell you, but I didn't waste any time on trying to find an explanation. I merely thanked her for ringing and hung up. Then I phoned the Grand, received a negative reply to my inquiry, and this hotel was my second call."

"Yes," Helen broke in urgently. "What time did my husband go to Lily's?" She was mentally calculating, remembering that the trains from Birmingham were very frequent.

"She didn't say, but she did say she'd been trying for hours to get me."

"You didn't go home when you left me?"

He shook his head; the brooding expression she had seen earlier settled on his face.

"I've been wandering about," he admitted, and without being invited to do so he took possession of a chair.

Helen's heart was thudding painfully.

"He could already be at your house," she quivered.

163

"Oh, I shouldn't think he could have come up so quickly as all that."

"He could –" She flashed him a glance. "You'd better go! If he should find you here. . . ." Her voice trailed away to a terrified silence as she heard the voice of the night porter.

"You can't just come up and enter the lady's room, sir –"

Abruptly he was cut short. Helen trembled from head to foot as she heard the sheer undiluted savagery in her husband's voice,

"Out of my way! I've told you – it's my wife I've come to see!"

The bedroom door was flung wide and Nick stood there, his smouldering eyes sweeping over the seated figure of Paul before settling on his wife's colourless face.

"Madam," began the porter, but she waved him away, scarcely aware of what she did. He went, and the door was kicked closed by the man standing just inside it. Paul stood up; it was clear that he too was afraid, for he edged away, putting some distance between him and the towering figure with the massive shoulders and piercing eyes – dark and dangerous as simmering pitch.

"Well?" he said softly, taking a slow step towards her. She opened her mouth, but the dryness of terror strangled the words in her throat. She seemed dazed by this terror, as if nature were about to take over and render her the relief of oblivion. Her mind made some attempt to fight this off and absurdly she found herself pondering on the irrelevant question of how he had managed to get here. But of course he too must have rung the

164

hotels. . . . Yes . . . and he had suspected that she would have Paul with her. The idea brought tears of anger and frustration to her eyes. She suddenly hated Paul for coming here. There had been no need for him to do so; he could have rung her, warning her that Nick was in England. Turning her attention to him, she saw to her amazement that his expression, though holding an element of fear, was in the main one of gloating satisfaction. So that was it! His action in coming here, in suggesting that they talk in the bedroom, had been deliberate; he had meant to be here when Nick arrived!

"Nick," she said desperately, finding her voice at last. "Nick, this situation isn't what it appears to be –" She took a step forward, forgetting her fear as she extended pleading hands towards him. "Hear me – please hear what I have to say." Her lovely blue eyes, slanting so very attractively, pleaded even as her voice had done. But her husband's mouth remained tight, his powerful jaw flexed, his eyes burning with fury.

"I'm ready and waiting *to* hear you," he told her gently. "If you can give me any reasonable explanation for having this man in your bedroom then I am willing to accept it."

Terror seized her again; this gentle tone . . . how deadly it was!

"Paul came only to warn me of your presence in England." What else could she say? Her eyes turned to Paul; she said quiveringly, "You explain – and truthfully. I never agreed for you to come to my room –"

"Never agreed?" echoed Paul, feigning astonishment and a shade of censure. "But how else would I be here?"

"You detestable creature –!" Helen was cut short, for

165

already Nick had covered the distance between him and Paul and he had him held by the lapels on his coat. Paul made a protest and twisted his body, but his strength was puny by comparison to that of the man who held him.

"Who are you?" demanded Nick, automatically shaking him. "How long have you known my wife?"

"I knew her before her marriage to you!" Paul seemed reckless, and it struck Helen that he was even willing to take whatever Nick chose to give so long as he could cause an insurmountable rift between him and his wife. And she was correct in her assumption, for it all came pouring from his lips. "She fell in love with me on our first meeting and I with her! But I was engaged to her best friend and she tried to fight it, running off to Birmingham to get away from me. I got married – like a fool – but later told Helen I was having a divorce so that I could marry her. Only this afternoon she admitted that she'd never have considered marriage to you had it not been for the dire necessity of putting a barrier between herself and me." He paused as Helen cast him a glance of bitter accusation. But she could not deny the turth of what he said and so she held her tongue. "So you see," Paul continued gloatingly, "she married you because she loved me – and for no other reason! She knew that if she didn't erect this barrier she'd betray her friend –"

"I don't believe you!" Nick flung Paul from him, and watched as, unable to keep his balance, he fell back on to the bed. "You're lying!" he snarled, but there was that in his tone which betrayed the fact that he was merely endeavouring to save his face. The humiliation he must be enduring was so totally new to him that he had not reached the point where he would admit to its presence at all. Helen quaked, aware that it was she who would suffer for what her husband was having to endure.

"Lying, am I?" Paul got up from the bed and his mouth curved in a sneer. In a flash of revelation Helen knew that Fran was better off without such a man for her husband. Yes, much better off, and now Helen actually hoped that the marriage would break up, for although Fran would suffer greatly, she would be fortunate in the long run, for she must surely find someone more worthy of her. Paul would never make a good husband, and Helen felt sure that what had already occurred would occur again and again. Paul would fall in love with others – if what he felt for Helen could be called love, she added as an afterthought. "Lying? Ask her, then! Go on – ask her why she married you! Look at her –" Wildly he pointed. "There isn't any need to ask her, is there? Guilt's written all over her face! She used you," he sneered. "Yes, she used you for her own ends. I asked her at the time if she had told you this, if she had informed you that her heart was given to another –" He turned to Helen, no sign of love in his eyes, but hate, bitter venomous hate. "Do you remember my asking you these questions?"

She said chokingly,

"You're unbelievably vindictive. How can you lie about your reason for coming here tonight? Tell my husband the truth –"

A harsh laugh cut her short.

"Still trying to deceive him? He's no fool; he's accepted that you were willing for me to stay here tonight –" He got no further; Nick's hand shot out and he

167

was once again seized in an inescapable grip.

"Open that door!" he ordered, and Helen swiftly did as she was told. Paul cast her a baleful glance before he was thrust unceremoniously from the room and the door slammed upon him.

Nick turned; she expected to see a snarl on his face, steeled herself for some onslaught – physical or otherwise. But to her utter amazement he seemed to have become drained of emotion. Certainly the fury that had blazed in his eyes had died, leaving in its place a sort of bitter disillusionment. He stared at her for a long while before he said,

"It was the truth, wasn't it? You made use of me – married me because you loved him?"

"It wasn't quite like that –"

"Not quite?"

"I admit I married you in order to prevent Paul from breaking up his marriage – You see, he had declared emphatically that he was going to divorce Fran. She was having a baby; and when Paul said that, had I also been married, the difficulties would have been much greater, I – I decided to accept your offer."

The dark eyes smouldered again, but dully this time. And his shoulders seemed not so erect as usual. Was it possible that he was hurt? wondered Helen, half inclined to tell him that whatever the reason for her marrying him she loved him now. But somehow she felt he would never believe her. She had lied to him so many times. It was only to be expected that a confession of love now would be taken as an attempt to smooth out the terrible situation in which she found herself at this moment.

"You were in love with him." A statement; Helen instantly denied this, but was told she was lying.

"If you weren't in love with him you'd only to tell him so and he'd have left you alone. You encouraged him in the first place; that's very plain."

"I didn't," she began, then stopped. Nick glanced at her face, saw the colour rise and said,

"Don't lie any more. You've done enough of that."

She said tremulously,

"I know now that it wasn't love I felt for him." He made no comment and she continued, "I do admit that, when we first met, there was a mutual attraction of some kind. But although at that time it frightened me, making me believe that, had it not been for Fran, Paul and I would have – have come together, I soon realized that it wasn't love I felt for him. And," she added, "it's now obvious that Paul doesn't care for me."

Nick continued to stare at her.

"You must have loved him." He paused and she thought he sighed inwardly. "Perhaps you still do. You came here to see him –"

"Only to tell him once and for all that I didn't want anything to do with him. In his letter he wrote of his intention of leaving his wife; he also said he was coming over to Greece to see me. I became so worried and – and desperate that I just had to see him. . . ." Helen allowed her voice to fade, for Nick was looking so contemptuously at her that she was left in no doubt at all that he believed her to be lying yet again.

"There doesn't seem to be anything more to say," she murmured after a long silence. And then, her voice breaking, "Do you – do you want us t-to part?"

"Part?" The black eyes ignited and they might have

169

belonged to Satan himself. "Part?" he repeated with a snarl. "No, my girl! There'll be no break-up of *our* marriage. A failure it might be, but it's still permanent. You're mine! Dare to leave me and you'll regret it for the rest of your life!"

CHAPTER TEN

DURING the weeks that followed Helen often recalled her husband's threat – that if she dared to leave him she would regret it for the rest of her life. Did he mean that he would do her some injury? She somehow could not imagine this, even though he was a man of so intense and strong emotions.

"Whatever his threat meant," she told herself one evening when, left alone for the third time in five days, she was sitting on the patio staring out into the dimness of the garden, "I shall have to leave him if things go on like this."

No violence now; no accusations or glances of contempt. Just indifference – cold and complete. Often she had tried to reach him, but the armour he had donned was impenetrable. He had no need for her either; he never came near her, never betrayed desire, never looked at her with the admiration to which she had become so used during those first months of their marriage.

Once he had said that he was beginning to think it was something more than her beauty that attracted him. If only everything had continued smoothly from there! If only Paul had kept out of her life. . . .

If. . . . What good were wishes or regrets? What was done could never be put right and it seemed that the only sensible course was to make a complete break.

"I can't," she cried inconsistently. "Not loving him as I do."

"Mrs. Nikolas. . . ." Katina's voice broke into her unhappy thoughts and she turned her head. "Dinner is ready."

Dinner – alone. She shook her head.

"I'm sorry, Katina, but I'm not hungry."

"Not hungry?" The gentle tone had the effect of bringing tears to Helen's eyes. Katina was sorry for her. And in all probability Julia and Costas were also sorry for her. "It is a very good dinner, Mrs. Nikolas. We have done the chicken in wine."

"Yes – I'm sure it's excellent, but, Katina, I don't want any dinner."

The girl hesitated, then shrugged her shoulders.

"Very well, Mrs. Nikolas. But Julia will be upset, you know."

"Tell her to keep it till tomorrow. We'll have it for lunch."

Katina spread her hands.

"It will not be the same." But she went away, and Helen was once more left alone.

Time passed and eventually she could stand the solitude no longer. Putting on a thin coat, she went out to take a long walk in the lanes surrounding the grounds. They were delightful, lined with perfumed flowers and wild rose trees. Oleanders followed the dry stream beds and pomegranate trees mingled with the olives and carobs on the lower slopes of the mountain. Above, pines flourished, and over it all the moon spread an ethereal beauty that transformed the scene to one of magic and romance. It was typically a Greek atmosphere, with the whirring of cicadas and the balmy breeze drifting through the trees and flowers, spreading their perfume. It was a place for lovers. . . . Suddenly the hot tears fell on to Helen's cheeks, tears of which she was ashamed but could not control, tears that for a long while had been locked in a cloud of misery and despair.

Reaching a little rise, she sat down, finding a handkerchief with which to dry her eyes. But the tears came again and again until she felt she must look a dreadful sight with her red cheeks and the swellings that must inevitably have appeared beneath her eyes. There was no one to see, she thought, so what did her appearance matter? A terrible loneliness came over her, like a destructive deluge – and she knew without a trace of doubt that she could not continue like this any longer. She would make a break. Nick had asked for it and so she knew no qualms of conscience at her decision. After all, what had happened in her life before she met him was her own affair; she had never questioned him about his past – which was far more reprehensible than hers! In fact, she had nothing at all of which to be ashamed; what had happened on her meeting with Paul was due to one of those mischievous tricks of fate, but she had acted honourably, resisting any temptation that had come to her at that time. Of course, Nick's chief cause for complaint was what had happened since, but as he was unwilling to listen to what she had to say there was no way in which she could vindicate herself. In any case, she thought with a sort of desolate resignation, he no longer wanted her, was no longer susceptible to her beauty as he had been at first, when desire had been so strong that he had forfeited the freedom he had so long valued, and held on to.

It was late when she arrived back; in the meantime tears had flowed again and again and she entered the house quietly, making for her room, having no desire that she should be seen by one of the servants. They were curious enough already –

"Mrs. Nikolas! You have returned." Katina appeared, much to Helen's disgust. "You –"

"I don't require any supper, thank you, Katina." Keeping her face turned from the girl, Helen added a brief good night and would have left her, but Katina's next words brought her swinging round, dismay gathering on her face.

"Mrs. Vakotis is come to see yourself and Mr. Nikolas."

"Mrs. Vakotis. . . ." Helen had never seen her mother-in-law since that night when her appearance had saved her from the amorous intentions of Nick. She had brushed past the woman, Helen recalled, icily ordering her to get out of the way so that she could reach the front door, and so make her escape. She had been spending her time visiting her numerous relations scattered all over Greece, Nick had told his wife on her asking where his mother was. Her home was in Corfu, but she spent little of her time there.

"She's quite likely to turn up at any time – be it convenient or otherwise," he had ended with a wry smile.

Well, she had certainly turned up at an inconvenient moment this time, thought Helen with a deepening frown.

173

"I have shown her into the living-room," smiled Katina, and with that familiar little bobbing movement she turned and left her mistress standing there wondering what she was going to say to her mother-in-law.

The moments passed as Helen's uncertainty continued. However, as Mrs. Vakotis could not be left there any longer Helen took off her coat, threw it over the back of a chair, and went along to the living-room, a beautiful apartment of luxury and good taste, with a panoramic view over the extensive front garden to the thickly-wooded hills beyond. The window was open and moths and other nocturnal insects had flown in to circle the several silver-gilt lamps with which the room was illuminated.

"Ah. . . ." The Greek woman had been standing admiring a lovely animal picture by Landseer, but at Helen's entry she swung about, tilting her dark head and subjecting her daughter-in-law to a critical and searching scrutiny. "Nikolas's wife. Where is my son?" Her dark eyes were fixed with a most curious expression on Helen's face and only now did Helen become aware of her appearance. For the moment she had completely forgotten that the evidence of her recent tears must still remain. However, it was too late to do anything about it and, spreading a hand, she invited Mrs. Vakotis to sit down, having first noticed that she had already discarded her coat and hat.

"Nikolas is out, I'm afraid," she added in reply to the woman's question. And on noting that she raised her eyebrows inquiringly Helen added, "He – er – was called away. . . ." It wasn't convincing and she decided not to add anything to this brief explanation. Mrs. Vakotis said with a frown, pointedly ignoring the last few words,

"Out? Already?"

"Already?" repeated Helen uncomprehendingly. "I don't know what you mean?" But the meaning came as she was speaking and she went red. "Nick's out on business," she then added with a touch of anger.

"Business, eh. . . ." almost to herself. And there followed an impatient click of her tongue. "Nick should never have considered marriage," she added bluntly. "Tell me, child, why did he marry you?" The dark piercing eyes were again taking in the clear evidence of Helen's unhappiness, and the frown on Mrs. Vakotis's forehead deepened until it became a dark furrow of anxiety.

"I don't think I wish to answer that question," returned Helen with dignity. "Can I get you some refreshment? You've had a long journey?" She was thinking of the words the woman had spoken on that unforgettable evening in Athens. She had travelled a long way and was famished and thirsty, she had told her son.

"I will merely take some wine."

"Very well." Moving over to the cabinet, Helen asked what Mrs. Vakotis would like.

"On second thoughts," came the rather angry response, "I think I'll have a double whisky."

Helen obligingly gave her what she wanted, then sat down on the couch, feeling awkward and wondering just how long it would be before her husband returned.

"Are you staying the night?" The question came before Helen gave the matter any thought. Glancing at the clock and discovering that it was almost half-past ten, she added quickly, "Of course you must be." A swift glance around and then, "You haven't any luggage?"

"It's in the hall." The dark eyes were fixed again, and searching. Anger appeared in them suddenly. "I rather think I shall stay for a little while." Something significant in her tone brought a flicker of inquiry to Helen's eyes and Mrs. Vakotis went on, "I've been talking to Katina while I was waiting for someone to come in, and I have learned that my son leaves you almost every night –"

"Not every night. Katina had no right to gossip to you, Mrs. Vakotis. She shall hear from me about it!"

The dark brows shot up.

"I have known Katina for many years, Helen. I employed her parents at one time. She was not gossiping, but merely chatting. I hope you will not give her a scolding because of it?"

Helen bit her lip. She felt angry and awkward and embarrassed all at once, for there was something just as arrogant and superior about this woman as there was about her son, and Helen felt inadequate – an inferior almost, hence her mixed and uncomfortable emotions. Had it not been for the fact that she had always adhered to a code of good manners she would have excused herself and left her mother-in-law sitting here, to await the arrival of her son.

"Nick doesn't leave me almost every night," she said at last. "It's only when of necessity he is called away."

"Necessity?" with another lifting of her brows, a gesture so very reminiscent of her son when in one of his sarcastic moods. "Helen, my dear," continued the woman softly, "I have known my son a lot longer than you. I'm no fool that I can be fobbed off with fairy tales – as Nick will soon discover when he returns. I shall demand to know why he married you and then decided he can

176

carry on as before! I am angry, Helen, and when I am angry I can be even more formidable than my son!"

Diverted Helen said, shaking her head vigorously,

"I think not, Mrs. Vakotis. I might, as you say, not have known Nick very long, but several times I have seen his temper."

Faintly her mother-in-law smiled, and the eyes became pensive. Helen suddenly decided she could like the woman – like her exceedingly.

"It's inevitable that you've seen his temper. He got it from me, and although I deplore the fact that I passed it on to him there is nothing I can do about it."

Helen had to laugh despite the way she was feeling.

"Heredity is something none of us can control, unfortunately."

Mrs. Vakotis was staring into her glass. She appeared so deeply engrossed with her thoughts that Helen began to wonder if she had heard what had been said to her.

"Do you still not wish to tell me the reason for the marriage?" she inquired at last, and for a long moment no reply was forthcoming. But Helen was not only feeling more at ease, she was also feeling warmer towards her mother-in-law. In any case, to avoid an answer would serve no profitable purpose; Mrs. Vakotis obviously knew there had been unusual circumstances surrounding the marriage of her son and the English girl who on their first meeting had treated her so rudely.

"He offered marriage because I wouldn't agree to – to become his – his pillow friend," she admitted, and another faint smile touched the firm outline of Mrs Vakotis's mouth.

"How like my son to go to these lengths to get what

177

he wanted! Never have I known him to let anything beat him." Mrs. Vakotis took a long drink, raising her eyes to Helen's face. "And you . . .? You must have had a reason for accepting his proposal of marriage?"

Helen said after a thoughtful pause,

"Has it not occurred to you that I might have been in love with Nick?"

Without hesitation the woman shook her head.

"No, my dear," she replied smoothly, "it hasn't." And she looked straightly at Helen as she spoke.

A soft flush rose; Mrs. Vakotis's expression became appreciative, for despite the puffiness that still disfigured her face Helen's beauty was most impressive.

"I can't tell you why I married him," she said at last. "I'm sorry. . . ."

"So whatever the reason you gave my son it was not the correct one," returned Mrs. Vakotis with the same swift perception her son would have shown, and Helen gave a start. She had not stopped to think that her refusal to say why she had married Nick would in itself have been so revealing. "I wish you would confide in me," added her mother-in-law presently. "I'm really a most understanding person, Helen, in spite of my rather forbidding exterior." Smiling as she said this, she took another drink which left the glass empty. She held it out and Helen rose to take it from her. To her surprise she heard Mrs. Vakotis say she would like the same again.

"Are you sure you wouldn't like something to eat?" Helen then asked, but Mrs. Vakotis shook her head.

"I'll have some supper when that son of mine gets in." Her eyes lifted to the clock on the wall. "Have you any idea when that will be?"

178

Helen shrugged.

"He won't be long," she said hopefully.

A lengthy silence ensued while she was even yet again examined by those very dark eyes.

"Why have you been crying?" The question came at last; Helen had somehow known that it would be asked. She was unable to find anything that would sound feasible and so she just dumbly shook her head. "You're in love with the wretch, aren't you?" came the staggering question then, a question that was in effect a statement, and to her dismay and chagrin Helen started to cry again. "Why," said her mother-in-law with some asperity, "didn't you agree to be his pillow friend? It would have been much less wearing on the nerves. And you'd not have been so unwise as to fall in love with him. What are your intentions?"

Helen dried her eyes and said firmly,

"I'm leaving him."

"I see." A pause and then, "You've come to the conclusion that he's spending his time with other women?"

"I can't think where else he could be," responded Helen frankly.

Thoughtfully her mother-in-law said,

"You know, marriage was not a step my son ever considered taking until he met you –"

"He would have married some time," interrupted Helen. "He told me that when the time came for marriage he would choose a Greek woman – for she would know her place," added Helen with some bitterness not unmingled with scorn – scorn for the Greek women who submitted so meekly to the tradition of male dominance.

"Know her place?" A smile appeared then. "I never

179

knew mine! I had wealthy parents who educated me. When I married I made it clear to Nick's father that I was no spineless little girl from the East who was ready and willing to lie down and allow him to wipe his feet on her. And let me tell you –" Mrs. Vakotis wagged a finger in Helen's direction. "Let me tell you, my dear, that a girl without spirit would bore my son in less than a week. That's why I said he had no interest in marriage. He might have said he preferred one of his own kind, but when it came to the point he would have shirked marriage with a Greek." A pause, but Helen made no comment. "Won't you tell me why you married him?" she asked again.

"I –" Helen stopped and frowned. "No – no, I can't tell you –"

"You can," gently and persuasively, "and I think you will, my dear.'

Helen looked at her through misty eyes. With every passing moment she was being more and more drawn to the woman sitting there, looking so superior and immaculate, so austere, in fact, that she appeared as unapproachable as her son at his most forbidding. Yet there was that about her that appealed, and Helen was acutely aware of the fact that her husband's personality was the same. He too possessed some underlying traits that appealed, that portended a gentleness and understanding which at first would seem totally alien to his nature as displayed by the uncompromising veneer he so often wore.

"I told Nick that I married him for security and – and money," said Helen at last, and her mother-in-law merely nodded and murmured softly,

"Yes, dear, but it's the real reason I'm interested in."

180

Helen swallowed, still hesitant. But at last she decided to tell her mother-in-law the whole story, and when she had done so she felt much much better. It was good to confide in someone, she thought, fluttering a smile which was meant to convey her gratitude. A responding smile came spontaneously, but there followed a frowning silence before Mrs. Vakotis said,

"It's all very unfortunate, Helen. You would have made my son an excellent wife. Must you leave him?"

"Of course," tremulously and with a rapid blinking of her eyes. What was wrong with her that she was so tearful? Helen asked herself angrily. "I can't go on like this. In any case, I expect Nick's hoping I'll leave; he'll then have complete freedom again."

"It appears he's got complete freedom as it is." But the words were automatic and Helen could see that Mrs. Vakotis was deep in thought. However, she was not able to say anything more, for at that moment Nick entered with his key and seconds later he was standing in the doorway of the living-room staring at his mother.

"Well," she said at length when he remained silent, "why don't you act with your usual lack of hospitality and ask what in the name of Hades I am doing here?"

He laughed then, but without humour. His black eyes moved to his wife's face; a frown appeared on his brow and she realized that he had taken in the fact that she had been crying.

"How long have you been here?" he inquired of his mother.

"Ages. No one to greet me! You out and Helen also –"

"Helen out?" sharply and with another glance in his wife's direction. "Where were you, then?"

So arrogant the tone. How alike these two people were!

"I went for a walk."

"I see." Going over to the cabinet he poured himself a drink, unaware of the piercing scrutiny he was receiving from his mother, who could see his face in the mirror. "You're staying for a while?" he asked, turning, and his mother nodded.

"May I ask where you have been?" she said softly, and his eyes became brooding and – could it be sad? wondered Helen unbelievingly. There was certainly a tired and hopeless air about him, she realized.

"Out," he replied briefly, then apologized for his absence. "You should have let me know you were coming," he added. "I would then have been here to receive you."

"You haven't told me where you've been?"

"Does it matter?" His glance flickered to his wife. He said casually, "You and Mother have been having a pleasant chat, I hope?" Subtle the question; Helen was not in the mood to converse any more and, rising, she announced her intention of going to bed.

"You and your mother will like to be alone for a while," she smiled, and after adding a brief good night she was gone.

But, once in her room, she found she was wide awake and, knowing that it would be useless to go to bed, she opened the window and stepped out on to the balcony. The night was balmy and soft as down; the air smelled sweetly of flowers. From a hillside the lonely braying of a donkey broke the silence now and then as it too was denied sleep – perhaps owing to hunger or thirst. For charming as the Greek people were, they had no idea how

182

to treat their animals. They seemed to think they had no feelings, that bodily discomforts could be endured without pain.

So engrossed was Helen by the cries of the donkey that for a while nothing else registered on her mind. She forgot completely that her husband had warned her not to go on to the balcony, as worm had got into the wooden supports and he had been negotiating with a firm in Mytilene about the dismantling of the balcony and the build-of a new one. And so it was only when she heard the warning creak and felt the floor giving way beneath her that she remembered Nick's words. But it was too late; with a cry of terror she flung out her arms in a frantic and futile attempt to find something to cling to.

"Nick!" she screamed as she went hurtling down to the garden below. "Nick. . . ." An excruciating pain shot through her head as she caught it on something hard and sharp. But she had fallen into thick, closely-growing shrubs and apart from some cuts and bruises on her arms and legs she felt that no damage had been done. It was a miracle, she thought, shuddering as she recalled that most of the balconies hung over paved walks or the sides of a courtyard.

"Helen!" Nick's voice, loud and anxious and sort of hollow-sounding. She tried to call in response, but the pain in her head increased and all she managed was a low agonized moan.

"Nick – the balcony! Look, it's given way. She must have fallen – Oh, God, she's not – not. . . ." The voice of Mrs. Vakotis faded and Helen thought she heard a loud intake of her breath that could almost be a sob.

"I'm all right," managed Helen at last in hurried re-

assuring tones. "I'm not hurt much ... not really...."
The pain in her head! It was excruciating, and another
low moan escaped her. She knew she was losing consciousness, but before total blackness enveloped her she
felt her husband's arms slide under her, felt herself
lifted from the tangle of shrubs into which she had
fallen. His shoulder cradled her head; his words came to
her as from beyond a deep impenetrable fog,

"Helen, my dearest...."

She was on the couch in the living-room when she came
to. Nick was there, and his mother, and a stocky Greek
who spoke in broken English.

"You've been lucky. You might have been killed."

"Yes...." Her eyes were on Nick; she wondered if
she were seeing aright, for his expression held tenderness
beyond her wildest dreams. "You called me dearest," she
murmured absurdly, forgetting the doctor altogether. "I
distinctly heard you...." The light was fading again and
she lifted a hand to clutch something – anything that
would help her to hold on to her consciousness.
"Nick...." He took her hand, holding it tightly. She
smiled tremulously and gave a sigh of relief as the light
drifted slowly back. "The bushes saved me," she said, remembering the doctor's words. "Yes, I was very lucky indeed."

"A few bruises and cuts," shrugged the doctor. "And
this rather nasty gash on your head, of course. It is
dressed for you and I will come again tomorrow. You will
be all right."

"Thank you, doctor," from Nick, who asked his
mother to show him out.

"Helen. . . ." Nick spoke almost before the door closed behind them. "I warned you about the balcony." His voice caught and to her amazement she actually heard a note of dread in it. "You might have been – been –" He broke off and Helen winced as his grip on her hand became like a vice.

"You – you were worried about me?" she asked breathlessly, even though she knew very well that such a question was quite unnecessary. The grey tinge that still remained about her husband's mouth was proof of this.

"Worried? Helen, you're my wife."

"Your wife. . . ." Her hand had dropped to the cover as Nick released it. Lifting it again, she silently begged him to take it, which he did, a thin smile touching the corners of his mouth. "I – I had begun to think that you – that you didn't want me for your wife any more."

He swallowed something tight in his throat.

"And so you were intending to leave me?"

She stared.

"How did you know?"

"Mother told me. She told me everything –"

"Everything?"

"I know you love me – Darling, why didn't you let me see how you felt?"

"How could I, when you didn't love me?" Her head was hurting and she realized that as a result of her pain she had injected a querulous note into her voice. "I thought you were beginning to love me, but then Harold spoiled it all and I saw that you didn't love me, and never would. So I decided the only sensible course was to go away."

He sighed and shook his head.

"It was because I already loved you that I had to know what you were keeping from me. Yes, I knew almost from the first that there was something. Then, later, there was the letter. I was mad with jealousy when you refused to show it to me because it was obvious that there was something of an intimate nature in it." He paused, but she merely looked apologetically at him. "You told Mother what was in it – in fact," he added with some asperity, "you told her everything there was to tell. Why on earth couldn't you have told it all to me?"

"Told it to you?" She tilted her head and added, "Nick, you know very well that I dared not."

At this he frowned and said,

"You mustn't ever be afraid of me, Helen."

She had to laugh.

"You say that – after terrorizing me the way you have?"

"Darling –" He sat down on the edge of the couch, lifting her hand to his lips. "Were you really frightened of me?"

"Dearest Nick," she returned, "you have the shortest of memories. How could I be anything else but frightened when you treated me the way you did?"

He became frowningly thoughtful.

"It must have been my infernal jealousy," he owned at last.

Allowing that to pass, she said tentatively,

"When you went out in the evenings. . . ." She tailed off, suddenly admitting that she would rather not put the question, in case his answer – or the deliberate evasion of an answer – should tell her that her suspicions had been correct. But he was frowning darkly now, as he gazed

186

into her face, and she knew that perception had already dawned.

"Just what are you wanting to know?" he asked in a changed tone. "Well?" he added after a long hesitation on her part.

"I th-thought that p-perhaps you —" She had to break off, for his expression was as dark as she had ever seen it.

"— were with another woman?" he finished for her in harsh and brittle accents.

"Don't be angry," she pleaded. "I couldn't think what else you could be doing — all that time."

Silence. He seemed incapable of speech. Letting go of her hand, he rose and walked away from the couch.

"How could you think that?" he demanded at length. "Hadn't I already told you that I didn't agree with a married man going out with other women?"

She nodded unhappily.

"I couldn't think what you could be doing," she repeated in a subdued voice. "I expect I was so miserable that I automatically wanted to make myself more miserable by imagining things. You do, Nick, when everything looks so bleak and hopeless. You imagined things yourself," she added as the thought occurred to her. "For one thing, you imagined I was in love with Paul, and you also imagined I went to England for a very different reason from the real one." She stopped because he had turned again and was coming back, the harshness having left his face.

"We've both been fools," he declared, taking her into his arms as she eased herself up on the couch. "And if Mother hadn't repeated all you told her we'd have gone on being fools." He smiled then, the tenderest of smiles, and his lips claimed hers in a long and ardent kiss. "My love," he said eventually, "I was merely riding about in the car, feeling as miserable as a man condemned, and wanting to come back to you, but my pride wouldn't let me. Besides, I wanted to hurt you, to make you feel lonely and neglected. But I hurt myself too, for the hours dragged on and on. They seemed endless!" He shuddered at the memory and tears welled up to moisten Helen's eyes.

"Nick. . . . Oh, I am so sorry –" The rest was silenced by his kiss and it was much later when he said, veering the subject a little,

"Darling, didn't you ever suspect that I loved you? Don't you recall, for instance, the occasion when I said that it was something more than your beauty that attracted me?"

Helen nodded against his shoulder.

"Yes, I do recall it." A small pause and then, "And do *you* recall what happened immediately afterwards?"

Nick frowned and shook his head, and Helen went on,

"I began to say that what you felt for me might be love. But at that moment Harold came into the room and I couldn't finish what I was saying."

"Harold." Nick's mouth tightened. "The trouble that man has caused us!" Helen said nothing and Nick went on, much more softly, "So you were, at that time, ready to own that you loved me?"

She nodded, a tender smile fluttering.

"Yes, I was ready," was her simple and brief reply.

"My dearest – if only I had known; what a lot of unhappiness we'd both have been saved."

"There were so many misunderstandings," she mused, then added contritely, "My lies didn't help. But at the time they all seemed so necessary."

Understandingly he nodded, and by his total lack of censure Helen knew just how cleverly his mother had related everything to him. Little had she known when confiding in her mother-in-law that she was in fact paving the way to the point where all misunderstandings would be smoothed out, and all mistakes forgiven.

"There'll be no such necessities in future," he said fervently, "because neither of us will have anything to hide."

Helen merely nodded her agreement and nestled close against her husband's breast. His arms tightened lovingly; she thrilled to the possessive hardness of his mouth as it was pressed to hers.

"Dearest Nick," she whispered huskily when at length he allowed her an opportunity to speak, "I love you so very much –" She broke off and drew away swiftly as the door opened and Mrs. Vakotis seemed as though she was about to enter. But she halted, stared for a long moment at the couple on the couch and then, quite casually,

"I'm rather pleased with my evening's work. Good night, my children. I'll see you in the morning," and after allowing a satisfied little smile to hover on her lips for a moment she quietly withdrew, closing the door noiselessly behind her.

Mills & Boon's Paperbacks

AUGUST

ACROSS THE LAGOON by ROUMELIA LANE

A lighthearted love story set in Venice in summer.

NO QUARTER ASKED by JANET DAILEY

Rich girl Stacey was trying to sample "real life". Why should Cord Harris be so disapproving?

DARK MOONLESS NIGHT by ANNE MATHER

Caroline had turned Gareth down once. Now they were to meet again. How would each of them feel after so long?

THE TOWER OF THE CAPTIVE by VIOLET WINSPEAR

Rafael and Vanessa had opposing attitudes towards the amount of freedom women should have. What would happen if they fell in love?

BACHELORS GALORE by ESSIE SUMMERS

Marty had *not* gone to New Zealand to find a husband. But she was a very attractive girl . . .

THE YELLOW MOON by REBECCA STRATTON

How could Catherine bear to hand over her little brothers to a man none of them knew?

STARS OVER SARAWAK by ANNE HAMPSON

In the jungle of Sarawak, Carl had saved Roanna's life – and a tribal saying declared that that life now belonged to him . . .

McCABE'S KINGDOM by MARGARET WAY

Katia had given up her career to look after her mother – but her step-brother Thorn was to prove a much bigger problem!

THE PAPER MARRIAGE by FLORA KIDD

Brooke and Meredith had married "on paper only". Suppose one of the marriage partners fell in love?

SONG CYCLE by MARY BURCHELL

Would family troubles prevent Anna from succeeding in the musical career on which she had set her heart?

20p net each

FREE!

YOUR COPY OF OUR MAGAZINE "HAPPY READING" AND CATALOGUE OF MILLS & BOON ROMANCES NOW AVAILABLE ON REQUEST

Over the page are listed 30 selections from our current catalogue. Why not contact your local stockist to obtain these books? However, should you have any difficulty please write to us at MILLS & BOON READER SERVICE, P.O. BOX 236, 14 Sanderstead Road, S. Croydon, Surrey, CR2 0YG, England*, ticking the titles you require, and enclosing your remittance. All Mills & Boon paperbacks ordered through the Reader Service are 20p. Please note to cover the postage and handling, will United Kingdom readers add 2p per book. Overseas readers are asked to add 10p per book and use International Money Orders where possible.

Please send me the free Mills & Boon Romance magazine ☐

Please send me the titles ticked ☐

I enclose £...(No C.O.D.)

Name.. Miss/Mrs

Address ....

Town/City ....

County/Country................................. Postal/Zip Code.............

MB7/74

HAVE YOU MISSED ANY OF THESE MILLS & BOON ROMANCES?

ALL PRICED AT 20p. SEE OVER FOR HANDY ORDER FORM. PLEASE TICK YOUR REQUIREMENTS